200 Words
You Need to Know

Kathy Sammis

J. WESTON

WALCH

PUBLISHER

Portland, Maine

User's Guide
to
Walch Reproducible Books

As part of our general effort to provide educational materials which are as practical and economical as possible, we have designated this publication a "reproducible book." The designation means that purchase of the book includes purchase of the right to limited reproduction of all pages on which this symbol appears:

Here is the basic Walch policy: We grant to individual purchasers of this book the right to make sufficient copies of reproducible pages for use by all students of a single teacher. This permission is limited to a single teacher, and does not apply to entire schools or school systems, so institutions purchasing the book should pass the permission on to a single teacher. Copying of the book or its parts for resale is prohibited.

Any questions regarding this policy or requests to purchase further reproduction rights should be addressed to:

Permissions Editor
J. Weston Walch, Publisher
321 Valley Street • P. O. Box 658
Portland, Maine 04104-0658

1   2   3   4   5   6   7   8   9   10

ISBN 0-8251-3738-1

Copyright © 1987, 1998
J. Weston Walch, Publisher
P. O. Box 658 • Portland, Maine 04104-0658

Printed in the United States of America

Contents

  • Safety Word Sense • Fun Fill-ins • (continued): Bonus! • Hidden Words
  • Lucky Lists • Puzzle Time • What's Missing? • Daffy Definitions
  • (continued): Bonus! • Sentence Sense • (continued): Bonus!

  • Personal Care Word Sense • Fun Fill-ins • (continued): Bonus! • Hidden Words
  • Lucky Lists • Puzzle Time • What's Missing? • Daffy Definitions
  • (continued): Bonus! • Sentence Sense • (continued): Bonus!

  • Body Word Sense • Fun Fill-ins • (continued): Bonus! • Hidden Words
  • Lucky Lists • Puzzle Time • What's Missing? • Daffy Definitions
  • (continued): Bonus! • Sentence Sense • (continued): Bonus!

  • Clothing Word Sense • Fun Fill-ins • (continued): Bonus! • Hidden Words
  • Lucky Lists • Puzzle Time • What's Missing? • Daffy Definitions
  • (continued): Bonus! • Sentence Sense • (continued): Bonus!

  • Weather Word Sense • Fun Fill-ins • (continued): Bonus! • Hidden Words
  • Lucky Lists • Puzzle Time • What's Missing? • Daffy Definitions
  • (continued): Bonus! • Sentence Sense • (continued): Bonus!

  • Entertainment Word Sense • Fun Fill-ins • (continued): Bonus! • Hidden Words
  • Lucky Lists • Puzzle Time • What's Missing? • Daffy Definitions
  • (continued): Bonus! • Sentence Sense • (continued): Bonus!

To the Teacher

200 Words You Need to Know is a set of vocabulary activity exercises designed for students with special needs. Two hundred words are divided into ten units of twenty words each, grouped into categories. Each unit contains ten masters with eight different vocabulary exercises to reinforce students' learning. Repetition with variety is the key: Each exercise is different but presents the student with each of the twenty vocabulary words to recognize and/or write. Bonus activities on some sheets encourage students to complete longer exercises.

The words themselves are common ones students need to master as part of everyday life—for their own personal safety or health, and in order to be competent consumers, job seekers, money handlers, car operators. Mastery of these words will boost students' self-image and confidence outside the schoolroom.

Exercise 1, Word Sense, introduces the unit's vocabulary words with simple definitions; students rewrite each word in the blanks provided. As a bonus, those students who can rewrite the boxed letters at the bottom of the page will discover a sentence related to the word category.

Exercise 2, Fun Fill-ins (two pages), encourages students to write the vocabulary words again in the blanks provided, using context clues and letters provided to choose the correct word for each sentence.

Exercise 3, Hidden Words, presents a simple paragraph containing all the vocabulary words for students to locate, and then provides them with practice in writing each word.

Exercise 4, Lucky Lists, has students classify the vocabulary words, by subject or by initial letter. You may have students alphabetize the words in each grouping after they have completed the classifying; answers are given in alphabetical order for your convenience should you choose this option. On those sheets classifying by initial letter, you may suggest students

write each letter included in the column at the head of the column—for example, for a column reading "Begins with a letter between *A* and *D*," students could write out the letters *A, B, C,* and *D* before attempting to classify the vocabulary words in the list.

Exercise 5, Puzzle Time, presents a simple puzzle grid. Students use initial letters and word length to fit each word into its appropriate set of puzzle boxes. When words have the same initial letter and length, a second letter is filled in so students can select the correct word for that set of puzzle boxes. The puzzle contains a light-hearted message related to the word category, reading from top to bottom of the puzzle grid. As a bonus, students are asked to find the "secret silly sentence" in the puzzle and rewrite it at the bottom of the page.

Exercise 6, What's Missing?, again provides students with the opportunity to choose the correct word from context clues, this time without individual letter blanks or letter clues. The last six sentences are set off as bonus activities to encourage students who may be intimidated by a list of twenty sentences to complete.

Exercise 7, Daffy Definitions, reinforces students' knowledge of the meanings of the vocabulary words by asking them to choose the correct definition from three given. The second page is marked BONUS! to encourage students.

Exercise 8, Sentence Sense, uses context clues to test and reinforce students' knowledge of word meanings by asking students to identify the one correct ending to each sentence from three given. Again, the second page is marked BONUS!

You may make as many copies as you want of each master, so students can work on each exercise as often as necessary to master it. You will find that the later units have somewhat more difficult words than the earlier units. Flash cards could help students who are having difficulty with particular words or categories.

To heighten student interest and motivation, an illustrated cover sheet is provided for each unit. To make this set into a series of ten mini-workbooks, reproduce the cover of each unit along with the exercise sheets, then staple cover and work sheets together. Making the work sheets into booklets keeps exercises organized by category and allows students to keep their completed work for review and display. You may wish to encourage your students to color their workbook covers with colored pencils, markers, or crayons. Or have your more creative students design their own workbook covers.

Optional Activities: Below is a series of optional activities designed to appeal to varying types of learning modalities, including visual, bodily/kinesthetic, logical, musical, and interpersonal. Use some or all of these activities to expand the scope of this book's reproducible activity sheets and draw in all types of learners.

- Make flash cards of the words in a unit.
  - Students can use the flash cards independently or with a partner to study all of a unit's words, or words/units particular students may be having difficulty with.
  - Have students (alone or in groups) use the flash cards as manipulatives. Ask students to alphabetize the cards, divide them into categories, or sort them by word length and/or part of speech.
  - Use the flash cards as appropriate in the other optional activities below.
- Ask musically inclined students to use a unit's words in a song. Students should choose a simple, familiar melody. They should use as many unit words as possible, but at least eight to ten. Students could then perform their songs for the class. This could be a group or individual activity.
- Challenge students, alone or in a group, to create a simple crossword puzzle using at least eight to ten words in a unit.
- Have students draw or bring in to class

pictures of a unit's words. Then play a quiz game involving pairs or groups of students, or the whole class. A partner, a group member, or you shows a picture to the other partner, other groups, or the class for oral or verbal identification. You could use flash cards for this, with students drawing or attaching a picture to the back of the word side of the card.

- Set up a group or individual scavenger hunt. Give students lists or flash cards of unit words and have them find actual examples of things representing the words in the school and community. Students list the location and give a description of each item found.
- Have students write their own unit word stories like the ones in the Hidden Words activities.
- Have students, alone or in groups, act out one of the Hidden Words stories, or one of the students' own stories.
- Play a game of charades. Divide the class into groups. Give each group the same number of words from a unit (flash cards would work well for this). Have groups, and individuals within groups, take turns acting out a unit's words for other groups.
- Divide students into pairs. One partner says a unit word aloud. The other partner writes it down. Both partners check to see if the word is written correctly. The partners continue through all or part of a unit's words, alternating between being the speaker and being the writer. Have each student keep a list of missed words and study them. You or partners could repeat this exercise after students have had time to study the missed words, checking for increased accuracy.

I hope both you and your students will enjoy working with *200 Words You Need to Know* and that your students will be encouraged by the successes they experience.

—*Kathy Sammis*

Vocabulary List

UNIT 1: SAFETY WORDS

closed	one way	slow	beware
danger	no trespassing	caution	fire alarm
flammable	yield	warning	slippery
detour	merge	poison	keep out
high voltage	information	hazard	stop

UNIT 2: PERSONAL CARE WORDS

hairbrush	toothbrush	haircut	makeup
bath	shave	shower	sponge
toothpaste	hair spray	floss	comb
lotion	razor	shampoo	prescription
soap	deodorant	mouthwash	powder

UNIT 3: BODY WORDS

head	leg	heart	throat
elbow	stomach	ankle	wrist
mouth	nose	chin	arm
shoulder	teeth	finger	chest
eye	skin	ear	knee

UNIT 4: CLOTHING WORDS

skirt	iron	boots	dry clean
jacket	underwear	button	bleach
zipper	shirt	shoes	dryer
pants	socks	sweater	jeans
panty hose	blouse	rinse	detergent

UNIT 5: WEATHER WORDS

snow	heat	drought	thunder
drizzle	sleet	lightning	rain
cloud	wind	forecast	sunny
flood	freeze	hurricane	fog
tornado	temperature	cold	ice

UNIT 6: ENTERTAINMENT WORDS

stereo	video	computer	cinema
cassette	VCR	sport	dance
game	radio	hobby	television
album	cable	concert	admission
movie	tape	CD	theater

UNIT 7: CAR WORDS

license	fuel	windshield	automobile
mph	engine	brakes	muffler
seat belt	ignition	hood	toll
coolant	gas	tire	speed limit
register	oil	headlight	inspection

UNIT 8: SHOPPING WORDS

payment	refund	installment	customer
discount	rebate	sales tax	price
guarantee	defect	return	purchase
exchange	layaway	sales slip	charge
sale	warranty	shoplift	credit card

UNIT 9: MONEY WORDS

deposit	cent	service charge	balance
dollar	quarter	amount	withdraw
money order	passbook	savings	interest
bill	cash	dime	account
nickel	coin	ATM	check

UNIT 10: JOB WORDS

wages	worker	bonus	paid holiday
sick leave	employment	tax	salary
benefits	employer	insurance	income
vacation	workplace	minimum wage	hourly
employee	overtime	supervisor	paycheck

Answer Section

UNIT 1: SAFETY WORDS

Exercise 1: Safety Word Sense

The message reads: Safety signs can help us.

Exercise 2: Fun Fill-ins

1. caution
2. no trespassing
3. poison
4. slippery
5. keep out
6. high voltage
7. danger
8. warning
9. flammable
10. fire alarm
11. merge
12. beware
13. detour
14. yield
15. closed
16. information
17. hazard
18. stop
19. slow
20. one way

Exercise 3: Hidden Words

My family once went on a trip filled with every kind of <u>hazard</u> and <u>danger</u>. The roads were <u>slippery</u> when we left home. This kept our speed <u>slow</u>. As we passed the <u>high-voltage</u> wires, a <u>fire alarm</u> began to ring. A sign ahead gave us <u>information</u>. It said, "<u>Caution</u>. Road <u>closed</u>. <u>Detour</u>." We had to <u>yield</u> to the other cars and merge onto a <u>one-way</u> street. Then we came to a <u>stop</u> sign. When we got to the campsite, we found more <u>warning</u> signs. They said, "<u>Keep out</u>. <u>No</u> <u>trespassing</u>. <u>Beware</u> of the <u>flammable</u> poison gas." What a trip!

Exercise 4: Lucky Lists

A–E: beware, caution, closed, danger, detour

F–J: fire alarm, flammable, hazard, high voltage, information

K–P: keep out, merge, no trespassing, one way, poison

Q–Z: slippery, slow, stop, warning, yield

Exercise 5: Puzzle Time

Secret sentence: Beware of slippery snakes.

```
                        B E W A R E
            D A N G E   R
            O N E ▮ W A Y
        F I R E ▮ A L A R M
            W A R N I N G
        M E R G E
                    O
                    F
            P O I S O N
                F L A M M A B L E
            C A U T I O N
    N O ▮ T R E S P A S S I N G
            S L I P P E R Y
            D E T O U R
        H A Z A R D
                Y I E L D
                S T O P
                I N F O R M A T I O N
H I G H ▮ V O L T A G E
                K E E P ▮ O U T
        C L O S E D
                S L O W
```

Exercise 6: What's Missing?

(#3 and #13 could be interchanged.)

1. beware	11. flammable
2. high voltage	12. danger
3. keep out	13. no trespassing
4. poison	14. hazard
5. fire alarm	15. detour
6. warning	16. stop
7. slippery	17. information
8. yield	18. merge
9. caution	19. one-way
10. slow	20. closed

Exercise 7: Daffy Definitions

1. a	6. b	11. a	16. c
2. b	7. a	12. a	17. a
3. c	8. a	13. c	18. a
4. c	9. c	14. b	19. b
5. b	10. b	15. b	20. c

Exercise 8: Sentence Sense

1. a	6. c	11. b	16. c
2. b	7. a	12. a	17. a
3. c	8. c	13. c	18. a
4. b	9. b	14. c	19. b
5. a	10. c	15. b	20. c

UNIT 2: PERSONAL CARE WORDS

Exercise 1: Personal Care Word Sense

The message reads: It's not hard to look good.

Exercise 2: Fun Fill-ins

1. haircut
2. toothbrush
3. toothpaste
4. prescription
5. makeup
6. razor
7. shampoo
8. bath
9. hair spray
10. shower
11. mouthwash
12. sponge
13. soap
14. deodorant
15. hairbrush
16. shave
17. lotion
18. comb
19. powder
20. floss

Exercise 3: Hidden Words

It wasn't easy for Bob to redo himself after ten years alone on a desert island! First he took a long <u>shower</u> and then a <u>bath</u>. He needed a <u>sponge</u> with plenty of <u>soap</u> and, of course, some <u>shampoo.</u> He worked for a long time with a <u>comb</u> and a <u>hairbrush.</u>

He still needed a <u>haircut</u> plus <u>hair spray</u> to make his hair look good. Next Bob took out his <u>razor</u> for a <u>shave.</u> He cleaned his teeth well with a <u>toothbrush,</u> <u>toothpaste,</u> and <u>floss.</u> He followed all that with <u>mouthwash.</u> He dusted <u>deodorant powder</u> under his arms. He rubbed his cuts with the <u>lotion</u> from his doctor's <u>prescription.</u> He even put a little <u>makeup</u> on his bruises. Now he was ready to greet his old friends!

Exercise 4: Lucky Lists

Cleaning and washing: bath, shower, soap, sponge

Hair care: comb, hairbrush, haircut, hair spray, shampoo

Mouth care: floss, mouthwash, toothbrush, toothpaste

Skin care and looks: deodorant, lotion, makeup, powder, razor, shave

Medicine: prescription

Exercise 5: Puzzle Time

Secret sentence: Do not comb the toothbrush.

Exercise 6: What's Missing?

1. sponge
2. hairbrush
3. shave
4. razor
5. lotion
6. comb
7. haircut
8. deodorant
9. makeup
10. floss
11. soap
12. prescription
13. bath
14. mouthwash
15. shower
16. toothbrush
17. shampoo
18. powder
19. hair spray
20. toothpaste

UNIT 3: BODY WORDS

Exercise 1: Body Word Sense

The message reads: A body lasts a lifetime.

Exercise 2: Fun Fill-ins

1. heart
2. chin
3. head
4. throat
5. skin
6. mouth
7. eye
8. ear
9. teeth
10. nose
11. knee
12. shoulder
13. arm
14. finger
15. leg
16. wrist
17. chest
18. elbow
19. ankle
20. stomach

Exercise 7: Daffy Definitions

1. a
2. c
3. a
4. b
5. b
6. a
7. c
8. b
9. c
10. a
11. a
12. b
13. c
14. b
15. c
16. a
17. a
18. c
19. c
20. b

Exercise 8: Sentence Sense

1. b
2. c
3. c
4. a
5. a
6. b
7. a
8. a
9. c
10. b
11. b
12. a
13. c
14. b
15. a
16. c
17. b
18. c
19. a
20. b

Exercise 3: Hidden Words

All parts of the body are useful. On top of your head is your scalp. The hair grows from here. You see with each eye and hear with each ear. You breathe and smell through your nose. Above your chin is your mouth, which has teeth for chewing. The food goes down your throat and into your stomach. From each shoulder grows an arm with an elbow and a wrist that bend. Each finger bends, too. The ankle and knee on the leg also bend. Inside your chest is your heart. It pumps blood. The whole body is covered with skin.

Exercise 4: Lucky Lists

Above the neck: chin, ear, eye, head, mouth, nose, teeth

From chin to legs: arm, chest, elbow, finger, heart, shoulder, stomach, throat, wrist

Below the stomach: ankle, knee, leg

All over: skin

Exercise 5: Puzzle Time

Secret sentence: I have no nose on my ankles.

```
C H I N
  T H R O A T
    A R M
    V
T E E T H
    N O S E
E L B O W
  K N E E
  S H O U L D E R
W R I S T
    H E A R T
    M O U T H
  F I N G E R
S T O M A C H
    E Y E
  H E A D
    A N K L E
    S K I N
      L E G
      E A R
C H E S T
```

Exercise 6: What's Missing?

1. chest
2. eye
3. ankle
4. stomach
5. teeth
6. arm
7. knee
8. nose
9. skin
10. mouth
11. shoulder
12. ear
13. head
14. finger
15. elbow
16. leg
17. throat
18. heart
19. wrist
20. chin

Exercise 7: Daffy Definitions

1. b
2. c
3. b
4. a
5. b
6. b
7. c
8. b
9. c
10. a
11. a
12. b
13. c
14. a
15. a
16. b
17. b
18. c
19. a
20. c

Exercise 8: Sentence Sense

1. a
2. c
3. c
4. b
5. a
6. a
7. c
8. b
9. b
10. a
11. b
12. c
13. b
14. a
15. a
16. c
17. b
18. b
19. a
20. c

UNIT 4: CLOTHING WORDS

Exercise 1: Clothing Word Sense

The message reads: Keep your clothes clean.

Exercise 2: Fun Fill-ins

1. shirt
2. shoes
3. skirt
4. socks
5. underwear
6. sweater
7. pants
8. button
9. panty hose
10. jacket
11. zipper
12. jeans
13. blouse
14. boots
15. dry clean
16. detergent
17. bleach
18. rinse
19. dryer
20. iron

Exercise 3: Hidden Words

Shanice bought lots of clothes for school. She got a pretty <u>blouse</u> to wear with her best <u>skirt</u>. She found a <u>shirt</u> and <u>sweater</u> to wear with her <u>pants</u> and her <u>jeans</u>. She bought a ski <u>jacket</u> and wool <u>socks</u> to keep her warm. She needed <u>panty hose</u> and <u>underwear</u>, too. She decided to wear last year's <u>shoes</u> and <u>boots</u>.

Then Shanice washed her dirty clothes. She used <u>bleach</u> and <u>detergent</u>. After the last <u>rinse</u>, Shanice checked each <u>zipper</u> and <u>button</u> to be sure they weren't broken. Then she loaded the <u>dryer</u>. She had to <u>iron</u> a dress. Some clothes she couldn't wash—she had to <u>dry clean</u> them instead.

Exercise 4: Lucky Lists

Upper body: blouse, jacket, shirt, sweater
Fasteners: button, zipper
Under outer clothing: panty hose, underwear
Lower body: boots, jeans, pants, shoes, skirt, socks
Taking care of clothes: bleach, detergent, dry clean, dryer, iron, rinse

Exercise 5: Puzzle Time

Secret sentence: I cannot button my zipper.

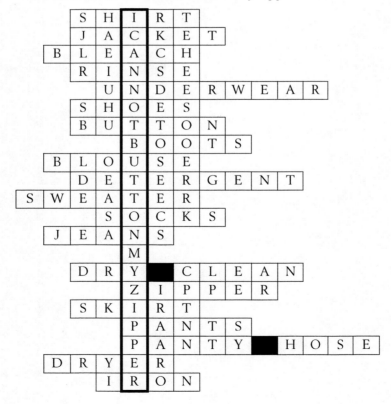

Exercise 6: What's Missing?

1. boots
2. rinse
3. zipper
4. pants
5. socks
6. skirt
7. jeans
8. dryer
9. button
10. blouse
11. shirt
12. panty hose
13. bleach
14. sweater
15. iron
16. jacket
17. dry clean
18. shoes
19. underwear
20. detergent

Exercise 7: Daffy Definitions

1. a
2. b
3. c
4. a
5. a
6. c
7. b
8. b
9. c
10. a
11. b
12. a
13. c
14. b
15. c
16. c
17. a
18. b
19. a
20. c

Exercise 8: Sentence Sense

1. c
2. a
3. b
4. b
5. c
6. a
7. a
8. c
9. b
10. b
11. c
12. a
13. c
14. b
15. b
16. a
17. a
18. c
19. b
20. c

UNIT 5: WEATHER WORDS

Exercise 1: Weather Word Sense

The message reads: Will the weather change?

Exercise 2: Fun Fill-ins

1. wind
2. thunder
3. heat
4. snow
5. temperature
6. flood
7. drizzle
8. freeze
9. cloud
10. sleet
11. tornado
12. hurricane
13. lightning
14. cold
15. rain
16. forecast
17. sunny
18. ice
19. drought
20. fog

Exercise 3: Hidden Words

Weather changes by the season. In the spring, it may <u>drizzle</u> one day and be <u>sunny</u> the next day. Sometimes there's too much <u>rain</u>, and it causes a <u>flood</u>. <u>Temperature</u> changes can create <u>fog</u>. Summer brings <u>heat</u> and puffy <u>clouds</u>, plus <u>thunder</u> and <u>lightning</u> storms. But sometimes there's too little <u>rain</u>, which causes <u>drought</u>. A <u>hurricane</u> or <u>tornado</u> can happen late in the summer or fall. In the winter, water can <u>freeze</u> into <u>ice</u>. <u>Snow</u> or <u>sleet</u> falls, and a <u>cold</u> <u>wind</u> blows. The weather <u>forecast</u> tells us when to expect these changes—but the <u>forecast</u> isn't always right!

Exercise 4: Lucky Lists

A–D: cloud, cold, drizzle, drought
E–H: flood, fog, forecast, freeze, heat, hurricane
I–S: ice, lightning, rain, sleet, snow, sunny
T–Z: temperature, thunder, tornado, wind

Exercise 5: Puzzle Time

Secret sentence: A cold cloud made fog freeze.

```
        H  E  A  T
 H  U  R  R  I  C  A  N  E
        S  N  O  W
        C  L  O  U  D
    W  I  N  D
        C  O  L  D
        L
     D  R  O  U  G  H  T
        S  U  N  N  Y
  F  L  O  O  D
     T  E  M  P  E  R  A  T  U  R  E
        R  A  I  N
  T  H  U  N  D  E  R
        S  L  E  E  T
        F  O  G
        O
     L  I  G  H  T  N  I  N  G
        F  R  E  E  Z  E
     T  O  R  N  A  D  O
  F  O  R  E  C  A  S  T
        E
     D  R  I  Z  Z  L  E
        I  C  E
```

Exercise 6: What's Missing?

1. thunder
2. wind
3. ice
4. lightning
5. snow
6. drought
7. rain
8. cloud
9. freeze
10. sunny
11. tornado
12. forecast
13. flood
14. temperature
15. hurricane
16. sleet
17. cold
18. fog
19. drizzle
20. heat

Exercise 7: Daffy Definitions

1. b	6. a	11. b	16. b
2. a	7. b	12. a	17. a
3. b	8. a	13. b	18. a
4. c	9. a	14. c	19. c
5. c	10. c	15. c	20. b

Exercise 8: Sentence Sense

1. a	6. c	11. c	16. a
2. c	7. a	12. b	17. c
3. b	8. a	13. b	18. b
4. b	9. c	14. c	19. b
5. a	10. b	15. a	20. a

UNIT 6: ENTERTAINMENT WORDS

Exercise 1: Entertainment Word Sense

The message reads: See a movie at the cinema.

Exercise 2: Fun Fill-ins

1. VCR	11. computer
2. radio	12. CD
3. album	13. theater
4. cassette	14. sport
5. cable	15. hobby
6. video	16. television
7. movie	17. cinema
8. stereo	18. concert
9. tape	19. dance
10. game	20. admission

Exercise 3: Hidden Words

I do many things to entertain myself. At home, I work on my <u>hobby</u> by putting stamps in my <u>album</u>. I may watch a <u>sports</u> event on <u>cable</u> <u>television</u> or watch a <u>video</u> on the <u>VCR</u>. I enjoy playing <u>games</u> on my <u>computer</u>, too. I often listen to a <u>CD</u> on the <u>stereo</u>. Sometimes I <u>tape</u> a song from the <u>radio</u> onto a <u>cassette</u>.

When I'm not at home, I like to see a <u>movie</u> at the local <u>theater</u>, which is called Mall <u>Cinema</u>. Sometimes I use a free pass for <u>admission</u>. I enjoy live music at a <u>dance</u> or a <u>concert</u>. Entertainment is relaxing and fun for me.

Exercise 4: Lucky Lists

Listening to music: album, cassette, CD, concert, radio, stereo, tape

Seeing something on a screen: cable, cinema, movie, television, theater, VCR, video

Something you play or do for fun: dance, game, hobby, sport

Entrance fees: admission

Powerful machine: computer

Exercise 5: Puzzle Time

Secret sentence: I sleep at the cinema. Do you?

Exercise 6: What's Missing?

1. hobby
2. television
3. stereo
4. concert
5. movie
6. cassette
7. theater
8. video
9. game
10. cinema
11. computer
12. cable
13. admission
14. VCR
15. dance
16. album
17. CD
18. tape
19. radio
20. sport

Exercise 7: Daffy Definitions

1. b
2. b
3. a
4. c
5. c
6. b
7. a
8. c
9. c
10. b
11. a
12. c
13. b
14. b
15. c
16. c
17. a
18. b
19. c
20. a

Exercise 8: Sentence Sense

1. a
2. c
3. c
4. b
5. a
6. b
7. b
8. a
9. c
10. c
11. b
12. a
13. b
14. c
15. c
16. a
17. a
18. b
19. b
20. c

UNIT 7: CAR WORDS

Exercise 1: Car Word Sense

The message reads: Change engine oil often.

Exercise 2: Fun Fill-ins

1. ignition
2. fuel
3. engine
4. license
5. oil
6. gas
7. mph
8. register
9. coolant
10. seat belt
11. hood
12. tire
13. muffler
14. toll
15. speed limit
16. headlight
17. brakes
18. inspection
19. automobile
20. windshield

Exercise 3: Hidden Words

After Kim got her driver's <u>license</u>, she bought an <u>automobile</u>. First she went to <u>register</u> the car. During <u>inspection</u>, important parts of the car were checked— the <u>muffler</u>, the <u>brakes</u>, each <u>headlight</u>, each <u>tire</u>, and each <u>seat</u> <u>belt</u>. Kim knew the <u>ignition</u> worked because the <u>engine</u> started right up.

Then she drove to a <u>gas</u> station for <u>fuel</u>. She raised the <u>hood</u> and checked the <u>oil</u> level and the <u>coolant</u>. She also cleaned the <u>windshield</u>. Then she drove her car home. On the way, she paid a <u>toll</u> and was careful to stay below the <u>speed</u> <u>limit</u> of 40 <u>mph</u>.

Exercise 4: Lucky Lists

Parts of a car: brakes, engine, headlight, hood, ignition, muffler, seat belt, tire, windshield

Liquids used in engine: coolant, fuel, gas, oil

Road signs and highways: mph, speed limit, toll

Owning and driving: inspection, license, register

Word for car: automobile

Exercise 5: Puzzle Time

Secret sentence: I feed my engine gas and oil.

```
I  G  N [I] T  I  O  N
M  U  F [F] L  E  R
T  I  R [E]
      F  U [E] L
H  O  O [D]
         [M] P  H
         [Y]
I  N  S  P [E] C  T  I  O  N
L  I  C [E] N  S  E
      E  N [G] I  N  E
H  E  A  D  L [I] G  H  T
         [N]
   S  P  E [E] D  ■  L  I  M  I  T
      R  E [G] I  S  T  E  R
      B  R [A] K  E  S
      G [A] S
      S  E [A] T  ■  B  E  L  T
C  O  O  L [A] N  T
      W  I [N] D  S  H  I  E  L  D
A  U  T  O  M [O] B  I  L  E
         [O] I  L
      T  O [L] L
```

Exercise 6: What's Missing?

1. gas	11. fuel
2. engine	12. speed limit
3. mph	13. hood
4. tire	14. oil
5. automobile	15. ignition
6. brakes	16. headlight
7. seat belt	17. register
8. toll	18. license
9. windshield	19. inspection
10. muffler	20. coolant

Exercise 7: Daffy Definitions

1. a	6. a	11. c	16. c
2. a	7. c	12. b	17. a
3. b	8. a	13. a	18. a
4. b	9. c	14. c	19. b
5. c	10. b	15. b	20. c

Exercise 8: Sentence Sense

1. a	6. b	11. b	16. b
2. c	7. b	12. b	17. b
3. c	8. a	13. c	18. a
4. a	9. c	14. a	19. c
5. a	10. c	15. c	20. c

UNIT 8: SHOPPING WORDS

Exercise 1: Shopping Word Sense

The message reads: You can be a wise shopper.

Exercise 2: Fun Fill-ins

1. warranty
2. sale
3. defect
4. guarantee
5. rebate
6. payment
7. exchanges
8. layaway
9. discount
10. refund
11. return
12. sales slip
13. credit card
14. purchase
15. charge
16. installment
17. sales tax
18. price
19. customer
20. shoplift

Exercise 3: Hidden Words

A smart shopper needs to know some basic facts. Check the <u>price</u> of each item you want to <u>purchase</u>. Can you buy the item on <u>sale</u> or at a <u>discount</u>? Is a <u>rebate</u> offered? Remember that your <u>payment</u> will include <u>sales tax</u>. Ask the store if a <u>customer</u> can <u>return</u> an item for a <u>refund</u> or an <u>exchange</u>. You'll probably need your <u>sales slip</u> to do this, so save it. Also find out if the item comes with a <u>warranty</u> or a <u>guarantee</u> against any <u>defect</u>.

Do you have enough cash to pay in full? If not, ask if you can put the item on <u>layaway</u> or <u>charge</u> it. If you use a <u>credit card</u>, you may be able to pay in <u>installments</u>. But of course, don't <u>shoplift</u>!

Exercise 4: Lucky Lists

A–D: charge, credit card, customer, defect, discount

E–L: exchange, guarantee, installment, layaway

M–R: payment, price, purchase, rebate, refund, return

S–Z: sale, sales slip, sales tax, shoplift, warranty

Exercise 5: Puzzle Time

Secret sentence: No refunds for shoplifters.

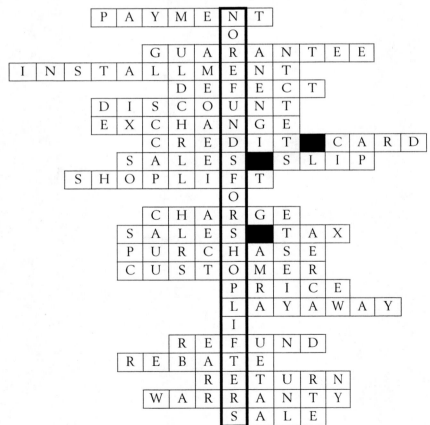

Exercise 6: What's Missing?

1. sale
2. discount
3. shoplifts
4. layaway
5. purchase
6. defect
7. price
8. installment
9. customer
10. rebate
11. refund
12. return
13. credit card
14. charge
15. sales tax
16. warranty
17. guarantee
18. sales slip
19. payment
20. exchange

Exercise 7: Daffy Definitions

1. a	6. c	11. a	16. a
2. c	7. c	12. a	17. b
3. b	8. b	13. b	18. c
4. b	9. a	14. b	19. c
5. a	10. c	15. c	20. a

Exercise 8: Sentence Sense

1. b	6. c	11. b	16. c
2. b	7. c	12. a	17. b
3. a	8. b	13. c	18. b
4. b	9. a	14. b	19. c
5. a	10. c	15. a	20. a

UNIT 9: MONEY WORDS

Exercise 1: Money Word Sense

The message reads: Pay in cash or use a check.

Exercise 2: Fun Fill-ins

1. dollar
2. dime
3. nickel
4. cent
5. coin
6. bill
7. money order
8. quarter
9. deposit
10. cash
11. account
12. savings
13. check
14. service charge
15. passbook
16. withdraw
17. balance
18. amount
19. interest
20. ATM

Exercise 3: Hidden Words

Yesterday I went to the bank to put some money into my <u>savings</u> <u>account</u>. First I counted the <u>coins</u>—each <u>cent</u>, <u>nickel</u>, <u>dime</u>, and <u>quarter</u>—and then the <u>dollar</u> <u>bills</u>. I wrote the total <u>amount</u> of <u>cash</u> on the <u>deposit</u> slip. I gave the slip and my <u>passbook</u> to the teller. When the teller gave me back the bankbook, it showed how much <u>interest</u> I had earned, and it also showed my new <u>balance</u>.

Today I had to <u>withdraw</u> some money, so I used the <u>ATM</u>. I also cashed a <u>check</u> and bought a <u>money order</u>. The bank collects a <u>service</u> <u>charge</u> when it cashes checks for people who don't have accounts at that bank.

Exercise 4: Lucky Lists

A–B: account, amount, ATM, balance, bill
C–H: cash, cent, check, coin, deposit, dime, dollar
I–P: interest, money order, nickel, passbook
Q–Z: quarter, savings, service charge, withdraw

Exercise 5: Puzzle Time

Secret sentence: Deposit a dollar or a dime.

```
        D I M E
      C H E C K
      D E P O S I T
        C O I N
  P A S S B O O K
        N I C K E L
  C E N T
        S A V I N G S
        D O L L A R
    A C C O U N T
      B A L A N C E
    B I L L
        C A S H
      Q U A R T E R
M O N E Y ■ O R D E R
    I N T E R E S T
        A M O U N T
  W I T H D R A W
        I
      A T M
S E R V I C E ■ C H A R G E
```

Exercise 6: What's Missing?

1. check
2. cash
3. cent
4. nickel
5. dime
6. quarter
7. bill
8. dollar
9. coin
10. money order
11. service charge
12. passbook
13. balance
14. withdraw
15. amount
16. ATM
17. interest
18. deposit
19. savings
20. account

Exercise 7: Daffy Definitions

1. a
2. a
3. c
4. b
5. c
6. a
7. b
8. b
9. c
10. a
11. c
12. b
13. c
14. a
15. a
16. b
17. b
18. c
19. a
20. b

Exercise 8: Sentence Sense

1. a
2. c
3. b
4. a
5. b
6. a
7. c
8. b
9. a
10. c
11. a
12. c
13. b
14. c
15. a
16. a
17. b
18. c
19. c
20. b

UNIT 10: JOB WORDS

Exercise 1: Job Word Sense

The message reads: Get to work on time daily.

Exercise 2: Fun Fill-ins

1. employee
2. employer
3. employment
4. wages
5. workplace
6. vacation
7. worker
8. bonus
9. benefits
10. sick leave
11. paycheck
12. minimum wage
13. paid holiday
14. insurance
15. income
16. tax
17. salary
18. overtime
19. hourly
20. supervisor

Exercise 3: Hidden Words

When you look for <u>employment</u>, you must ask some questions. What <u>salary</u> or <u>hourly wages</u> will you earn for a job? Will you still have enough <u>income</u> after <u>tax</u> is taken out of your <u>paycheck</u>? Does the job pay more than the <u>minimum wage</u>? Will you work and be paid for <u>overtime</u>? Ask the <u>employer</u> or <u>supervisor</u> what <u>benefits</u> each <u>employee</u> is given. Will you have health <u>insurance</u>? How often will you have a <u>paid holiday</u> and a <u>vacation</u>? Will you be paid when you're on <u>sick leave</u>? Can you expect a Christmas <u>bonus</u>? Also find out if each <u>worker</u> belongs to a labor union. Finally, look at where you'll be doing your job. Do the <u>workplace</u> conditions look good to you?

Exercise 4: Lucky Lists

A–E: benefits, bonus, employee, employer, employment

F–O: hourly, income, insurance, minimum wage, overtime

P–S: paid holiday, paycheck, salary, sick leave, supervisor

T–Z: tax, vacation, wages, worker, workplace

Exercise 5: Puzzle Time

Secret sentence: Workers want worthy wages.

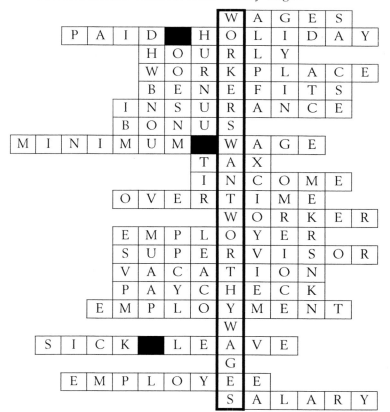

Exercise 6: What's Missing?

1. worker
2. employment
3. wages
4. overtime
5. minimum wage
6. benefits
7. employer
8. supervisor
9. employee
10. paycheck
11. hourly
12. salary
13. bonus
14. workplace
15. income
16. tax
17. insurance
18. sick leave
19. paid holiday
20. vacation

Exercise 7: Daffy Definitions

1.	b	6.	a	11.	c	16.	b
2.	c	7.	b	12.	b	17.	c
3.	c	8.	c	13.	b	18.	b
4.	a	9.	a	14.	a	19.	a
5.	b	10.	a	15.	a	20.	c

Exercise 8: Sentence Sense

1.	a	6.	b	11.	b	16.	c
2.	b	7.	b	12.	c	17.	b
3.	a	8.	a	13.	b	18.	a
4.	c	9.	c	14.	a	19.	c
5.	b	10.	c	15.	a	20.	b

Unit 1

SAFETY WORDS

EXERCISE 1
SAFETY WORD SENSE

Name _____

Date _____

Read each word below and its definition. Rewrite each word in the blanks next to its definition.

1. closed — not open; shut — _ _ _ [s] _ _

2. danger — the chance that something harmful will happen; or, something that causes harm — _ [a] _ _ _ _

3. flammable — able to catch on fire easily — [f] _ _ _ _ _ _ _ _

4. detour — indirect or roundabout way — _ [e] _ _ _ _

5. high voltage — very powerful electric current — _ _ _ _ _ _ _ _ [t] _ _

6. one way — going in only one direction — _ _ _ _ _ [y]

7. no trespassing — going onto this land or into this building is not allowed — _ _

_ _ _ _ _ _ _ [s] _ _ _

8. yield — to give way; to let another driver go first — _ [i] _ _ _

9. merge — join together and become one — _ _ _ [g] _

10. information — facts or knowledge about something — _ [n] _ _ _ _ _ _ _ _ _

11. slow — not fast; with little speed — [s] _ _ _

12. caution — close attention; or, a warning to be careful — [c] _ _ _ _ _

13. warning — notice to watch out for something — _ [a] _ _ _ _ _

14. poison — substance that is harmful if you eat, drink, or inhale it — _ _ _ _ _ [n]

15. hazard — something dangerous or risky — [h] _ _ _ _ _

16. beware — watch out; be careful — _ [e] _ _ _ _

17. fire alarm — device that makes a loud sound to warn of fire — _ _ _ _ _ [l] _ _ _

18. slippery — causing slipping and sliding — _ _ _ [p] _ _ _ _

19. keep out — do not enter — _ _ _ _ _ _ [u] _

20. stop — come to a halt; not move any more — [s] _ _ _

BONUS! The boxed letters spell out a sentence. What does it say? (Write it out here if you want:)

2

200 Words You Need to Know

FUN FILL-INS

Name _____

Date _____

Each sentence below has a word (or two words together) missing. Fill in each blank with a word that makes sense from the list at the top of this page. Check off each word in the list as you use it.

danger	caution	fire alarm
flammable	warning	slippery
high voltage	poison	keep out
	no trespassing	

1. Go forward with _ _ *u* *t* _ _ *n* , because the road is icy.

2. Mr. Grump hung _ *o* _ *r* *e* _ _ *a* _ *s* _ _ *g* signs all over his property.

3. A bottle with _ *o* *i* _ _ _ in it often has a skull and crossbones on the label.

4. The floors are _ *l* *i* _ *p* _ _ *y* just after they are mopped.

5. The neighborhood kids were warned to *k* _ _ _   _ *u* _ of the burned building.

6. The electric company posted large signs that said "_ _ *g* _

   _ *o* _ _ _ *g* _ ."

7. *D* _ _ _ *e* _ seems to face Luke Skywalker at every turn.

8. Teresa was given a _ _ *r* *n* _ _ *g* the second time she was late to class.

9. Be sure to keep _ _ *l* _ _ *m* _ *b* *l* _ clothing away from fire and stoves.

10. The _ _ *r* _   *a* _ *a* _ _ rang for five minutes before the firefighters arrived.

3

200 Words You Need to Know

Name _____

Date _____

(BONUS! Continue to fill in the blanks from the word list at the top of this page.)

hazard	yield	closed
merge	stop	slow
one way	detour	beware
	information	

11. This lane of traffic will __ __ *r* __ __ with another one soon.

12. Our field trip guide told us to __ __ *w a* __ __ of the poison ivy.

13. While the road was being repaired, the cars had to go on a long *d* __ __ *o u* __ .

14. You must __ *i* __ *l* __ to oncoming traffic when you enter a highway.

15. I went to the library after school, but it was *c* __ __ *s* __ __ .

16. If you don't know the phone number, call __ *n f* __ __ *m* __ *t i* __ __ .

17. *H* __ *z* __ __ __ is another word for danger.

18. When you come to the end of the road, __ *t* __ __ .

19. __ __ __ *w* down before stopping.

20. We could only go __ *n* __ __ *a* __ on that street.

4 *200 Words You Need to Know*

HIDDEN WORDS

Name _____

Date _____

Read the following story. Draw a line under the words from the list below when you find them in the story. Check off each word in the list as you find it. The first one is done.

✔ closed	one-way	slow	beware
danger	no trespassing	caution	fire alarm
flammable	yield	warning	slippery
detour	merge	poison	keep out
high-voltage	information	hazard	stop

My family once went on a trip filled with every kind of hazard and danger. The roads were slippery when we left home. This kept our speed slow. As we passed the high-voltage wires, a fire alarm began to ring. A sign ahead gave us information. It said, "Caution. Road closed. Detour." We had to yield to the other cars and merge onto a one-way street. Then we came to a stop sign. When we got to the campsite, we found warning signs. They said, "Keep out. No trespassing. Beware of the flammable poison gas." What a trip!

Now write each word you marked in the story on the lines below.

closed _____   _____   _____

_____   _____   _____

_____   _____   _____

_____   _____   _____

_____   _____   _____

_____   _____

Name _____

Date _____

Each word in the list at the top of this page belongs in one of the categories listed below. Write each word under the category it belongs to. The first one in each column is done for you. Check off each word in the list as you use it.

✔ closed	✔ one way	slow	beware	high voltage
danger	no trespassing	caution	fire alarm	information
✔ flammable	✔ yield	warning	slippery	hazard
detour	merge	poison	keep out	stop

Begins with a letter between *A* and *E*

closed

_____

_____

_____

Begins with a letter between *F* and *J*

flammable

_____

_____

_____

Begins with a letter between *K* and *P*

one way

_____

_____

_____

Begins with a letter between *Q* and *Z*

yield

_____

_____

_____

Name _____

Date _____

Fill in the boxes in the puzzle with words that fit from the word list at the top of this page. Check the words off in the list as you use them. The first letter (and sometimes another one) of each word is given. The first one is done for you.

closed	one way	slow	✔ beware	high voltage
danger	no trespassing	caution	fire alarm	information
flammable	yield	warning	slippery	hazard
detour	merge	poison	keep out	stop

BONUS! The puzzle has a secret silly sentence. It reads from the top of the puzzle down. Write the puzzle's secret silly sentence here:

_____

EXERCISE 6
WHAT'S MISSING?

Name _____

Date _____

A word (or two together) is missing from each sentence. Choose a word (or two together) from the list that makes sense and write it in the blank for each sentence. Check off each word in the list as you use it. The first one is done.

1. _*Beware*_ of the dog.

2. Electric wires! _____   _____ !

3. Don't come in—_____   _____ .

4. This is _____! Do not eat or drink!

5. In case of fire, pull the _____   _____ .

6. I'm _____ you! Don't pet the snake!

7. Floors are _____ when wet.

8. _____ to cars on the left.

9. Be careful—proceed with _____ .

10. _____ down on curves.

11. _____ fabrics may catch on fire.

12. There's _____ ahead—falling rocks.

13. Stay off any property with a _____   _____ sign.

14. Ice on the road is a _____ .

BONUS! If you have filled in all the blanks above, keep going and fill in these blanks, too.

15. Road closed; take a _____ .

16. A red light means _____ .

17. Your questions will be answered at the _____ booth.

18. _____ with the other traffic.

19. You can only drive in one direction on a _____

_____ road.

20. Road _____ ; take a detour.

closed

danger

flammable

detour

high voltage

one-way

no trespassing

yield

merge

information

slow

caution

warning

poison

hazard

✔ beware

fire alarm

slippery

keep out

stop

DAFFY DEFINITIONS

Name _____

Date _____

Choose the correct definition for each word. Circle the letter in front of the definition you choose.

1. closed
   - (a) shut
   - (b) items you wear
   - (c) open to the public

2. danger
   - (a) being mad
   - (b) something causing harm
   - (c) likely to catch on fire

3. flammable
   - (a) very poor
   - (b) good to eat
   - (c) likely to catch on fire

4. detour
   - (a) large truck
   - (b) dead end
   - (c) roundabout way

5. high voltage
   - (a) tall building
   - (b) powerful electric current
   - (c) important person

6. one way
   - (a) small wave
   - (b) in one direction only
   - (c) upside down

7. no trespassing
   - (a) keep out
   - (b) open
   - (c) welcome

8. yield
   - (a) give way
   - (b) call out loudly
   - (c) ask a question

9. merge
   - (a) leafy bush
   - (b) go in opposite directions
   - (c) join together

10. information
    - (a) odd shape
    - (b) facts about something
    - (c) party

200 Words You Need to Know

Name _____

Date _____

(BONUS! Continue to choose the correct definition for each word.)

11. slow
    (a) not fast
    (b) sloppy or messy
    (c) quick

12. caution
    (a) close attention
    (b) being reckless
    (c) political meeting

13. warning
    (a) getting hotter
    (b) mending clothes
    (c) notice to watch out

14. poison
    (a) jail
    (b) harmful substance
    (c) yellow-green color

15. hazard
    (a) African deer
    (b) danger or risk
    (c) three-wheeled bike

16. beware
    (a) recognize
    (b) dress well
    (c) be careful

17. fire alarm
    (a) warning device
    (b) red truck with a siren
    (c) clock that wakes you up

18. slippery
    (a) causing slipping and sliding
    (b) bumpy and rough
    (c) having flippers

19. keep out
    (a) come in
    (b) do not enter
    (c) close the door behind you

20. stop
    (a) cooking pans
    (b) spinning toys
    (c) come to a halt

SENTENCE SENSE

Name _____

Date _____

Choose an ending that makes sense for each sentence. Circle the letter in front of the ending you choose. The vocabulary word or words in each sentence are underlined.

1. There was danger ahead,
   (a) the guide warned us.
   (b) so we stopped being careful.
   (c) so we let the baby go first.

2. A flammable object
   (a) won't burn easily.
   (b) catches on fire easily.
   (c) is good to eat.

3. The high-voltage sign was
   (a) printed on the cereal box.
   (b) posted on the swimming pool.
   (c) attached to the electric pole.

4. The no trespassing sign
   (a) explained how to play the game.
   (b) meant we couldn't go on that land.
   (c) told us we could go into the woods.

5. Caution! tells you to
   (a) be careful.
   (b) hurry up.
   (c) eat quickly.

6. A sore throat is a warning sign
   (a) that you're getting better.
   (b) that you finished your dinner.
   (c) that you may be getting a cold.

7. If a bottle says "Poison,"
   (a) don't drink what's in it.
   (b) sprinkle the contents in your bath.
   (c) use it to run your lawn mower.

8. One hazard astronauts fear is
   (a) tasty and interesting meals.
   (b) a good night's sleep.
   (c) meteor showers.

9. The kids on our block have to beware of
   (a) the bowl of goldfish.
   (b) the fierce dog.
   (c) the friendly police officer.

10. Because the sign said "Keep Out,"
    (a) we went right in.
    (b) we drank the soda.
    (c) we knew we couldn't go in there.

(BONUS! Continue to choose the correct ending for each sentence.)

11. The sign said "Road Closed," so we
    (a) drove faster.
    (b) turned back.
    (c) kept on going.

12. A sign that says "Detour" means you must
    (a) take a different road.
    (b) stop for lunch.
    (c) pay a fine.

13. All cars on a one-way road
    (a) drive at a high speed.
    (b) drive with their headlights on.
    (c) drive in the same direction.

14. You often see a sign that says "Yield"
    (a) in a movie theater.
    (b) at the supermarket.
    (c) on the highway.

15. When two lanes of traffic merge,
    (a) they crash into each other.
    (b) they become one lane of traffic.
    (c) they drive away from each other.

16. The sign said "Go Slow," so I
    (a) drove as fast as I could.
    (b) took a nap.
    (c) drove at a slower speed.

17. When I heard the fire alarm, I
    (a) hurried out of the building.
    (b) ran into the burning building.
    (c) cheered.

18. Because the floor was slippery, my grandmother
    (a) fell down.
    (b) ate her dinner.
    (c) played soccer.

19. I went to the information booth because I needed
    (a) to buy an ice cream cone.
    (b) to find out where the bus station was.
    (c) to do my homework.

20. When you come to a stop sign, you must
    (a) keep your car moving.
    (b) turn around.
    (c) bring the car to a complete stop.

Unit 2
PERSONAL CARE WORDS

EXERCISE 1
PERSONAL CARE WORD SENSE

Name _____

Date _____

Read each word below and its definition. Rewrite each word in the blanks next to its definition.

1. hairbrush — tool with bristles and a handle used to smooth hair — _ _ [i] _ _ _ _ _

2. bath — a washing in water — _ _ [t] _

3. toothpaste — product used to clean and whiten teeth — _ _ _ _ _ _ _ [s] _ _

4. lotion — creamy liquid for the skin — _ _ _ _ _ [n]

5. soap — product used to clean and wash — _ [o] _ _

6. toothbrush — tool used to clean teeth — [t] _ _ _ _ _ _ _ _

7. shave — to cut off hair with a razor — _ [h] _ _ _

8. hair spray — product sprayed on to keep hair in place — _ [a] _ _   _ _ _ _ _

9. razor — tool with a sharp blade used to shave off hair — [r] _ _ _ _

10. deodorant — product used to stop smells — _ _ _ [d] _ _ _ _ _

11. haircut — trimming or cutting of hair — _ _ _ _ _ _ [t]

12. shower — a washing in sprayed water; or, to wash in sprayed water — _ _ [o] _ _ _

13. floss — string used to clean between teeth; or, to use this string — _ [l] _ _ _

14. shampoo — product used to clean hair; or, to use this product — _ _ _ _ _ _ [o] _

15. mouthwash — product gargled to make breath fresh — _ [o] _ _ _ _ _ _

16. makeup — products like lipstick used on the face to make it look better — _ _ [k] _ _ _

17. sponge — soft cleaning pad; or, to use this pad — _ _ _ _ [g] _

18. comb — tool with teeth used to smooth hair; or, to use this tool — _ [o] _ _

19. prescription — order for medicine written by a doctor — _ _ _ _ _ _ _ _ _ _ [o] _

20. powder — soft, fine material often dusted on the skin; or, to use this material — _ _ _ [d] _ _

BONUS! The boxed letters spell out a sentence. What does it say? (Write it out here if you want:)

14

Name _____

Date _____

Each sentence below has a word (or two words together) missing. Fill in each blank with a word that makes sense from the list at the top of this page. Check off each word in the list as you use it.

bath	hair spray	shampoo
toothpaste	razor	makeup
toothbrush	haircut	prescription
	shower	

1. After the *h* _ _ _ *c* *u* _ , her curls were quite short.

2. The dentist told Otis he needed a new _ *o* *o* _ _ *b* _ _ _ *h* with good bristles.

3. Most _ _ _ *t* *h* _ _ _ *s* *t* _ has fluoride to make teeth stronger.

4. My grandmother's *p* _ _ *s* *c* _ _ *p* _ _ *o* _ medicine is expensive.

5. Too much _ _ *k* _ *u* _ on your face—lots of eye shadow, for example—can look bad.

6. A dull _ _ *z* *o* _ can cause nicks and cuts on your skin.

7. *S* _ _ *m* _ *o* _ is better than soap for washing hair.

8. My baby sister has her _ _ _ *h* in that tiny tub.

9. Ramona used so much _ *a* _ _ _ *p* _ _ *y* , her hair felt stiff.

10. Rinse all the sand out of your hair in the _ *h* _ *w* _ _ .

200 Words You Need to Know

Name _____

Date _____

(BONUS! Continue to fill in the blanks from the word list at the top of this page.)

hairbrush	shave	sponge
lotion	deodorant	comb
soap	floss	powder
	mouthwash	

11. After eating onions and garlic, Uncle Felix rinsed his mouth out with

    _m_ _ _u_ _t_ _ _ _ _a_ _ _ .

12. A _ _p_ _ _n_ _ _ soaks up liquids.

13. Wash your hands with _ _o_ _ _ and water before meals.

14. The janitor sprayed with a room _d_ _e_ _ _ _o_ _r_ _ _n_ _ to keep the bathroom smelling fresh.

15. It's often easier to untangle hair with a _ _ _i_ _r_ _ _ _u_ _ _h_ than with a comb.

16. When does a boy usually begin to _ _h_ _ _v_ _ his chin whiskers?

17. Creamy _ _o_ _t_ _ _ _ helps smooth our dry and cracked skin.

18. A _ _ _ _b_ is easy to carry in your pocket to smooth out hair quickly.

19. The white _p_ _ _w_ _ _ _ she dusted on made her face look very pale.

20. You can buy waxed or unwaxed dental _ _ _l_ _ _s_ _ for cleaning between your teeth.

     200 Words You Need to Know

EXERCISE 3
HIDDEN WORDS

Name _____

Date _____

Read the following story. Draw a line under the words from the list below when you find them in the story. Check off each word in the list as you find it. The first one is done.

hairbrush	toothbrush	haircut	makeup
bath	shave	✔ shower	sponge
toothpaste	hair spray	floss	comb
lotion	razor	shampoo	prescription
soap	deodorant	mouthwash	powder

    It wasn't easy for Bob to redo himself after ten years alone on a desert island! First he took a long <u>shower</u> and then a bath. He needed a sponge with plenty of soap and, of course, some shampoo. He worked for a long time with a comb and a hairbrush. He still needed a haircut plus hair spray to make his hair look good. Next Bob took out his razor for a shave. He cleaned his teeth well with a toothbrush, toothpaste, and floss. He followed all that with mouthwash. He dusted deodorant powder under his arms. He rubbed his cuts with the lotion from his doctor's prescription. He even put a little makeup on his bruises. Now he was ready to greet his old friends!

Now write each word you marked in the story on the lines below.

shower _____   _____   _____

_____   _____   _____

_____   _____   _____

_____   _____   _____

_____   _____   _____

_____   _____   _____

_____   _____

LUCKY LISTS

Name _____

Date _____

Each word in the list at the top of this page belongs in one of the categories listed below. Write each word under the category it belongs to. The first one in most categories is done for you. Check off each word in the list as you use it.

✔ shampoo	soap	razor	floss	sponge
✔ bath	toothbrush	deodorant	hairbrush	comb
✔ toothpaste	lotion	haircut	mouthwash	prescription
✔ shave	hair spray	shower	makeup	powder

Words related to cleaning and washing

bath
_____
_____
_____
_____

Words related to hair care

shampoo
_____
_____
_____
_____

Words related to mouth care

toothpaste
_____
_____
_____

Words related to skin care and how you look

shave
_____
_____
_____
_____

Word related to medicine

_____

Name _____

Date _____

Fill in the boxes in the puzzle with words that fit from the word list at the top of this page. Check the words off in the list as you use them. The first letter (and sometimes another one) of each word is given. The first one is done for you.

hairbrush	soap	razor	floss	sponge
bath	toothbrush	deodorant	shampoo	comb
toothpaste	shave	haircut	mouthwash	prescription
lotion	hair spray	shower	makeup	✔powder

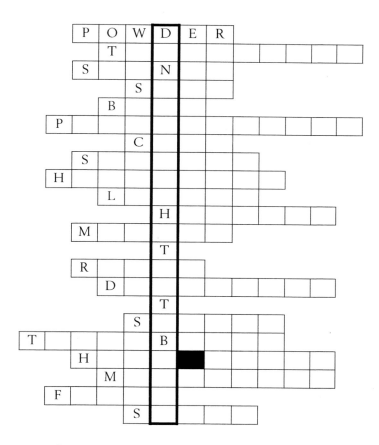

BONUS! The puzzle has a secret silly sentence. It reads from the top of the puzzle down. Write the puzzle's secret silly sentence here:

_____

200 Words You Need to Know

EXERCISE 6
WHAT'S MISSING?

Name _____

Date _____

A word (or two together) is missing from each sentence. Choose a word (or two together) from the list that makes sense and write it in the blank for each sentence. Check off each word in the list as you use it. The first one is done.

1. Use a __*sponge*__ to clean the bathtub.

2. Beatriz needs a _____ with soft bristles for her long hair.

3. Will Santa Claus _____ off his beard?

4. He uses a _____ to shave his chin.

5. Malik rubbed a soothing _____ on his skin.

6. I always carry a pocket _____ with small teeth.

7. Dad looked nearly bald after his _____ .

8. Do you use spray or roll-on _____ ?

9. Actors have to wear a lot of _____ .

10. Dentists always say it's important to _____ .

11. The bar of _____ floats in the bathtub.

12. To pick up the medicine, go to the _____ counter.

13. A hot _____ in a tub feels great.

14. _____ helps stop bad breath.

BONUS! If you have filled in all the blanks above, keep going and fill in these blanks, too.

15. She stood under the _____ to rinse off.

16. My dentist gave me a new _____ .

17. _____ cleans hair well.

18. Mom dusted _____ on the baby.

19. _____ _____ keeps my hair in place.

20. Squeeze the _____ onto the toothbrush.

hairbrush

bath

toothpaste

lotion

soap

toothbrush

shave

hair spray

razor

deodorant

haircut

shower

floss

shampoo

mouthwash

makeup

✔ sponge

comb

prescription

powder

200 Words You Need to Know

EXERCISE 7
DAFFY DEFINITIONS

Name _____

Date _____

Choose the correct definition for each word. Circle the letter in front of the definition you choose.

1. hairbrush
   - (a) tool used to smooth hair
   - (b) device used to dry hair
   - (c) evergreen bush

2. bath
   - (a) a trail to walk on
   - (b) air you draw into your lungs
   - (c) a washing in water

3. toothpaste
   - (a) product used to clean teeth
   - (b) candy in a tube
   - (c) frosting for a cake

4. lotion
   - (a) movement
   - (b) creamy liquid for the skin
   - (c) warm milk

5. soap
   - (a) to get very upset
   - (b) product used to clean and wash
   - (c) flat fish

6. toothbrush
   - (a) tool used to clean teeth
   - (b) tool used to smooth hair
   - (c) dentist's drill

7. shave
   - (a) trim a hedge
   - (b) wash in a spray of water
   - (c) cut off hair with a razor

8. hair spray
   - (a) high waterfall
   - (b) product used to control hair
   - (c) flower arrangement

9. razor
   - (a) tool used to raise flags
   - (b) small wild pig
   - (c) tool used for shaving

10. deodorant
    - (a) product to stop bad smells
    - (b) perfume
    - (c) product to clean hair

Name _____

Date _____

(BONUS! Continue to choose the correct definition for each word.)

11. haircut
    (a) trimming of the hair
    (b) brushing of the hair
    (c) shaving with a razor

12. shower
    (a) loud cry
    (b) a washing in sprayed water
    (c) tall building

13. floss
    (a) light foam
    (b) shiny glow
    (c) string used to clean teeth

14. shampoo
    (a) product used to clean teeth
    (b) product used to clean hair
    (c) small curly-haired dog

15. mouthwash
    (a) washcloth
    (b) product used to clean face
    (c) product used to make breath fresh

16. makeup
    (a) products used on the face
    (b) clothes and shoes
    (c) unmarried woman

17. sponge
    (a) soft cleaning pad
    (b) beach towel
    (c) tool for eating soup

18. comb
    (a) exploding device
    (b) tool used to clean teeth
    (c) tool used to smooth hair

19. prescription
    (a) word picture
    (b) recipe
    (c) order for medicine

20. powder
    (a) strength
    (b) fine, light material
    (c) thick stew

Choose an ending that makes sense for each sentence. Circle the letter in front of the ending you choose. The vocabulary word in each sentence is underlined.

1. I use a <u>toothbrush</u> twice a day
   (a) to smooth my hair.
   (b) to clean my teeth.
   (c) to wash my hands.

2. A sharp <u>razor</u>
   (a) is used to slice meat.
   (b) is easy to drive.
   (c) shaves smoothly.

3. My father used a large <u>sponge</u>
   (a) to dig in the garden.
   (b) to cook the turkey.
   (c) to mop up the spilled milk.

4. Her sister's <u>hairbrush</u>
   (a) has a round handle.
   (b) tastes good.
   (c) cleans teeth well.

5. Suntan <u>lotion</u>
   (a) helps prevent sunburn.
   (b) feels like sandpaper.
   (c) is hard as wood.

6. It's best to <u>floss</u>
   (a) before swimming.
   (b) after brushing your teeth.
   (c) for your mother's birthday.

7. You must have a doctor's <u>prescription</u>
   (a) to buy that medicine.
   (b) to get in to see that movie.
   (c) to brush your teeth.

8. <u>Deodorant</u> helps prevent an unpleasant smell
   (a) when you sweat.
   (b) at low tide.
   (c) in the park.

9. I squeezed the <u>toothpaste</u> out
   (a) into my hair.
   (b) onto my shoe.
   (c) onto the brush.

10. Matt likes to <u>shampoo</u>
   (a) his car on Saturdays.
   (b) his hair every day.
   (c) his homework before dinner.

Name _____

Date _____

(BONUS! Continue to choose the correct ending for each sentence.)

11. I gave a <u>bath</u> to my
    (a) schoolbooks.
    (b) little brother.
    (c) orange juice.

12. Hector used <u>soap</u> to
    (a) wash his face.
    (b) make the coffee.
    (c) brush his teeth.

13. Every morning, Kareem is sure to <u>shave</u>
    (a) his cat.
    (b) his basketball.
    (c) his face.

14. Nykesha used <u>hair</u> <u>spray</u>
    (a) to feed the tomatoes.
    (b) to keep her hair in place.
    (c) to polish the table.

15. I go to get a <u>haircut</u>
    (a) when my hair gets too long.
    (b) when my clothes don't fit.
    (c) when my arms get too long.

16. After taking a <u>shower</u>, I
    (a) am very dirty.
    (b) am asleep.
    (c) am wet and clean.

17. <u>Mouthwash</u> helps
    (a) your hair look shiny.
    (b) your breath smell good.
    (c) your room stay clean.

18. Yolanda wore <u>makeup</u>
    (a) on her teeth.
    (b) in her hair.
    (c) on her face.

19. Use a <u>comb</u> to
    (a) smooth out your hair.
    (b) clean your teeth.
    (c) feed the kitten.

20. The body <u>powder</u> Davika used
    (a) was wet and oily.
    (b) felt good on her skin.
    (c) went well with the spaghetti.

Unit 3
BODY WORDS

EXERCISE 1
BODY WORD SENSE

Name _____

Date _____

Read each word below and its definition. Rewrite each word in the blanks next to its definition.

1.	head	top part of the body	_ _ [a] _
2.	elbow	middle of the arm, where it bends	_ _ [b] _ _
3.	mouth	what you put food in and talk through	_ [o] _ _ _
4.	shoulder	what the arm is attached to	_ _ _ _ _ [d] _
5.	eye	what you see with	_ [y] _
6.	leg	what you stand on and walk with	[l] _ _
7.	stomach	organ that digests food	_ _ _ _ _ [a] _
8.	nose	what you breathe and smell with	_ _ [s] _
9.	teeth	hard white parts of the mouth used to bite and chew	[t] _ _ _ _
10.	skin	the body's outer covering	[s] _ _ _
11.	heart	organ that pumps blood	_ _ [a] _ _
12.	ankle	joint that connects the foot and leg	_ _ _ [l] _
13.	chin	front of the jaw, below the mouth and above the neck	_ _ [i] _
14.	finger	one of the five parts at the end of the hand	[f] _ _ _ _ _
15.	ear	what you hear with	[e] _ _
16.	throat	part of the neck that food passes through	[t] _ _ _ _ _
17.	wrist	joint that connects the hand and the arm	_ _ [i] _ _
18.	arm	body part between the shoulder and the hand	_ _ [m]
19.	chest	upper front part of the body	_ _ [e] _ _
20.	knee	middle of the leg, where it bends	_ _ _ _

BONUS! The boxed letters spell out a sentence. What does it say? (Write it out here if you want:)

200 Words You Need to Know

Each sentence below has a word missing. Fill in each blank with a word that makes sense from the list at the top of this page. Check off each word in the list as you use it.

head	teeth	chin
mouth	skin	ear
eye	heart	throat
	nose	

1. Samantha was so excited, her _h_ __ __ __ _t_ began to beat faster.

2. My grandfather's __ _h_ __ __ whiskers are long, curly, and pure white.

3. How could you wear a hat if you didn't have a __ _e_ __ __ ?

4. It hurts to swallow when you have a sore __ _h_ __ __ _a_ __ .

5. Very pale __ _k_ __ __ can burn badly in strong sun.

6. Marcus opened his _m_ __ __ __ __ and yawned loudly.

7. The kitten has one blue __ __ _e_ and one brown one.

8. My mother wears a hearing aid in her __ _a_ __ so she can hear what people say.

9. The dentist told us to brush our __ _e_ __ _t_ __ after every meal.

10. When I have a cold, my __ _o_ __ __ gets runny.

Name _____

Date _____

(BONUS! Continue to fill in the blanks from the word list at the top of this page.)

elbow   ankle   arm
shoulder   stomach   chest
leg   finger   knee
              wrist

11. It's easy to twist a _k_ _ _ _ when you're playing a sport.

12. A football player's _ _h_ _ _u_ _l_ _ _ _ pads make him look even bigger.

13. Ana stretched her _ _ _m_ as far as she could to reach the shelf.

14. Don't stir the hot soup with your _ _i_ _n_ _ _ _ !

15. My father's left _l_ _ _ always hurts before a rainstorm.

16. Rosalie wore a pretty gold bracelet around her _ _r_ _ _s_ _ .

17. Last week I had a head cold; this week I have a _c_ _ _ _s_ _ cold.

18. Her doll's arm bent at the wrist and the _ _ _b_ _ _w_ .

19. The water was so cold we only got wet up to the _ _n_ _k_ _ _ .

20. My dog loves to roll over on his back and have his _s_ _ _ _m_ _ _c_ _ rubbed.

HIDDEN WORDS

Name _____

Date _____

Read the following story. Draw a line under the words from the list below when you find them in the story. Check off each word in the list as you find it. The first one is done.

✔ head	leg	heart	throat
elbow	stomach	ankle	wrist
mouth	nose	chin	arm
shoulder	teeth	finger	chest
eye	skin	ear	knee

All parts of the body are useful. On top of your <u>head</u> is your scalp. The hair grows from here. You see with each eye and hear with each ear. You breathe and smell through your nose. Above your chin is your mouth, which has teeth for chewing. The food goes down your throat and into your stomach. From each shoulder grows an arm, with an elbow and a wrist that bend. Each finger bends, too. The ankle and knee on the leg also bend. Inside your chest is your heart. It pumps blood. The whole body is covered with skin.

Now write each word you marked in the story on the lines below.

head _____ _____

_____ _____ _____

_____ _____ _____

_____ _____ _____

_____ _____ _____

_____ _____

Name _____

Date _____

Each word in the list at the top of this page belongs in one of the categories listed below. Write each word under the category it belongs to. The first one in most categories is done for you. Check off each word in the list as you use it.

✔ head	eye	teeth	chin	wrist
✔ elbow	✔ leg	skin	finger	arm
mouth	stomach	heart	ear	chest
shoulder	nose	ankle	throat	knee

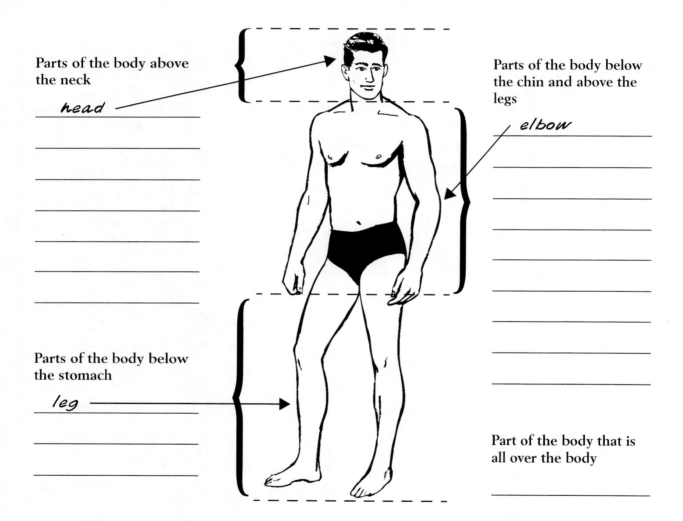

Parts of the body above the neck

head _____

_____

_____

_____

_____

_____

_____

Parts of the body below the chin and above the legs

elbow _____

_____

_____

_____

_____

_____

_____

_____

_____

Parts of the body below the stomach

leg _____

_____

_____

Part of the body that is all over the body

_____

BONUS! Draw a line from each word to its place on the body.

Fill in the boxes in the puzzle with words that fit from the word list at the top of this page. Check the words off in the list as you use them. The first letter (and sometimes another one) of each word is given. The first one is done for you.

head	eye	teeth	✔ chin	wrist
elbow	leg	skin	finger	arm
mouth	stomach	heart	ear	chest
shoulder	nose	ankle	throat	knee

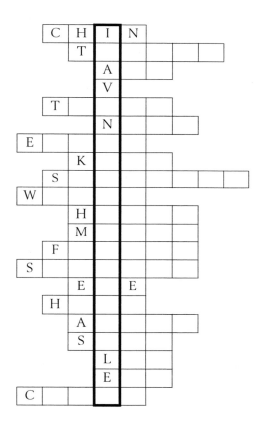

BONUS! The puzzle has a secret silly sentence. It reads from the top of the puzzle down. Write the puzzle's secret silly sentence here:

_____

WHAT'S MISSING?

Name _____

Date _____

A word is missing from each sentence. Choose a word from the list that makes sense and write it in the blank for each sentence. Check off each word in the list as you use it. The first one is done.

1. Take a deep breath through your throat into your
   chest _____ .

2. Ken blinked his left _____ .

3. Feet bend at the _____ .

4. My _____ growls when it's empty.

5. Tomas grinned to show us the braces on his _____ .

6. The sleeve is too short for my _____ .

7. High socks come up to your _____ .

8. I used my _____ to smell the roses.

9. _____ covers the whole body.

10. Father spooned food into the baby's _____ .

11. Each arm starts at a _____ .

12. Listen well with your _____ .

13. Shantay nodded her _____ to say yes.

14. The ring slipped off Ahmed's _____ .

BONUS! If you have filled in all the blanks above, keep going and fill in these blanks, too.

15. In the middle of each arm is an _____ .

16. Hop on one _____ .

17. Your _____ is inside your neck.

18. I could feel my _____ beating.

19. Your arm and hand join at the _____ .

20. Shave that beard off your _____ .

head

arm

leg

eye

ear

teeth

skin

chin

nose

shoulder

throat

finger

✔ chest

heart

knee

wrist

ankle

elbow

mouth

stomach

DAFFY DEFINITIONS

Name _____

Date _____

Choose the correct definition for each word. Circle the letter in front of the definition you choose.

1. head
   - (a) sandwich loaf
   - (b) top of the body
   - (c) feeling good

2. elbow
   - (a) what you hear with
   - (b) colored arch in the sky
   - (c) middle of the arm

3. mouth
   - (a) third month of the year
   - (b) opening to put food in
   - (c) lunch or supper

4. shoulder
   - (a) what the arm is attached to
   - (b) middle of the leg
   - (c) member of an army

5. eye
   - (a) myself
   - (b) what you see with
   - (c) what you chew with

6. leg
   - (a) young sheep
   - (b) what you stand on
   - (c) tall tree

7. stomach
   - (a) basement
   - (b) where the heart is
   - (c) where food is digested

8. nose
   - (a) what you see with
   - (b) what you smell with
   - (c) what you stand on

9. teeth
   - (a) help someone to learn
   - (b) sandy seashore
   - (c) what you bite and chew with

10. skin
    - (a) the body's outer covering
    - (b) black and white animal
    - (c) dark liquid to write with

Name _____

Date _____

(BONUS! Continue to choose the correct definition for each word.)

11. heart
    (a) organ that pumps blood
    (b) top part of the body
    (c) not tall

12. ankle
    (a) go fishing
    (b) joint between foot and leg
    (c) shiny stone

13. chin
    (a) foreign country
    (b) end of the foot
    (c) front of the jaw

14. finger
    (a) a part at the end of the hand
    (b) what you breathe with
    (c) baseball player

15. ear
    (a) what you hear with
    (b) what you see with
    (c) what you chew with

16. throat
    (a) high seat for a king or queen
    (b) what food passes through
    (c) what you think with

17. wrist
    (a) joint between leg and foot
    (b) joint between arm and hand
    (c) joint in the middle of the arm

18. arm
    (a) what you stand on
    (b) building for farm animals
    (c) part between shoulder and hand

19. chest
    (a) upper front part of body
    (b) lower part of body
    (c) joint between arm and hand

20. knee
    (a) insect with wings and a stinger
    (b) joint in the middle of the body
    (c) joint in the middle of the leg

SENTENCE SENSE

Name _____

Date _____

Choose an ending that makes sense for each sentence. Circle the letter in front of the ending you choose. The vocabulary word in each sentence is underlined.

1. I bought <u>elbow</u> patches
   - (a) to sew onto the sleeves of my jacket.
   - (b) to sew onto the legs of my pants.
   - (c) to sew onto the heels of my socks.

2. Jaleesa opened her <u>mouth</u>
   - (a) so she could hear the music.
   - (b) so she could smell the flowers.
   - (c) so the dentist could work on her teeth.

3. The dress hung from the girl's <u>shoulders</u>
   - (a) up to her scalp.
   - (b) down to her ears.
   - (c) down to her feet.

4. A strong <u>ankle</u> will help you
   - (a) sing clearly.
   - (b) run fast and easily.
   - (c) see long distances.

5. My uncle's <u>stomach</u> grew bigger
   - (a) because he ate lots of food.
   - (b) because he learned to play the piano.
   - (c) because I talked to him.

6. The wolf uses its sharp <u>teeth</u>
   - (a) to tear off pieces of meat.
   - (b) to climb tall trees.
   - (c) to smell other animals.

7. To listen to a <u>heart</u> beating, press your ear against
   - (a) a knee.
   - (b) another ear.
   - (c) the chest.

8. Food goes from the mouth through the <u>throat</u> and
   - (a) into the ear.
   - (b) into the stomach.
   - (c) into the elbow.

9. Snap your <u>wrist</u> when you
   - (a) kick a soccer ball.
   - (b) throw a baseball.
   - (c) shake your head.

10. There is one <u>knee</u>
    - (a) on each leg.
    - (b) on each arm.
    - (c) on top of the head.

         200 Words You Need to Know

Name _____

Date _____

(BONUS! Continue to choose the correct ending for each sentence.)

11. On my sister's <u>head</u> was
 (a) a pot of flowers.
 (b) a big straw hat.
 (c) a pair of shoes.

12. Thanks to my sharp <u>eyes</u>,
 (a) I heard every note that the band played.
 (b) I smelled the wonderful perfume.
 (c) I saw every detail of the game.

13. Use your <u>legs</u>
 (a) to throw the ball.
 (b) to run fast.
 (c) to eat your soup.

14. Without a <u>nose</u>, you could not
 (a) smell the flowers.
 (b) hear the birds sing.
 (c) taste the salsa.

15. Your <u>skin</u> is
 (a) on the outside of your body.
 (b) on the inside of your body.
 (c) usually green.

16. On my grandfather's <u>chin</u> was
 (a) a funny-looking monkey.
 (b) a finger.
 (c) a long white beard.

17. On your <u>finger</u> you can wear a
 (a) bathrobe.
 (b) ring.
 (c) boot.

18. I used my keen <u>ears</u>
 (a) to watch the movie.
 (b) to listen to the singer.
 (c) to run in the race.

19. Jerome has a strong <u>arm</u>, so he can
 (a) throw a baseball a long way.
 (b) kick a football a long way.
 (c) eat a lot of food.

20. The <u>chest</u> is
 (a) at the bottom of the leg.
 (b) on top of the head.
 (c) underneath the head and throat.

Unit 4

CLOTHING WORDS

EXERCISE 1
CLOTHING WORD SENSE

Name _____

Date _____

Read each word below and its definition. Rewrite each word in the blanks next to its definition.

1. skirt — girls' or women's clothing that hangs down from the waist
`_ [k] _ _ _`

2. jacket — short coat
`_ _ _ _ [e] _`

3. zipper — fastener with teeth and a slider
`_ _ _ _ [e] _`

4. pants — clothing for the lower body that covers each leg separately
`[p] _ _ _ _`

5. panty hose — one-piece stockings
`_ _ _ _ [y] _ _ _ _`

6. iron — device with a flat base you can heat, used to smooth or press clothes; or, to use an iron
`_ _ [o] _`

7. underwear — clothing you wear under outer clothes
`[u] _ _ _ _ _ _ _ _`

8. shirt — clothing for the upper body, usually with a collar and sleeves
`_ _ _ [r] _`

9. socks — soft covering for the feet
`_ _ [c] _ _`

10. blouse — clothing for the upper body, usually for girls and women
`_ [l] _ _ _ _`

11. boots — covering for the feet and lower legs, usually of rubber or leather
`_ _ [o] _ _`

12. button — small round fastener you pass through a hole or a loop
`_ _ [t] _ _ _`

13. shoes — outer covering for the feet
`[h] _ _ _ _`

14. sweater — warm, knitted clothing for the upper body
`_ _ [e] _ _ _ _`

15. rinse — to wash off with clear water
`_ _ _ [s] _`

16. dry clean — to clean clothes without water
`_ _ _ [c] _ _ _ _`

17. bleach — to make whiter or lighter; or, the powder or liquid you use to bleach
`_ [l] _ _ _ _`

18. dryer — machine used to dry wet clothing
`_ _ _ [e] _`

19. jeans — pants made from a strong cotton cloth
`_ _ [a] _ _`

20. detergent — powder or liquid used to wash clothes
`_ _ _ _ _ _ _ _ [n]`

BONUS! The boxed letters spell out a sentence. What does it say? (Write it out here if you want:)

200 Words You Need to Know

FUN FILL-INS

Name _____

Date _____

Each sentence below has a word missing. Fill in each blank with a word that makes sense from the list at the top of this page. Check off each word in the list as you use it.

skirt   underwear   button
jacket   shirt   shoes
panty hose   socks   sweater
                   pants

1. Nate wore a striped __ *h* __ __ __ with long sleeves under his sweater.

2. When I got to the beach, I took off my *s h* __ __ __ and socks and ran around in bare feet.

3. Her __ *k* __ __ __ was very full and hung down below her knees.

4. I wear two pairs of wool __ *o* __ *k* __ in the winter to keep my feet warm.

5. You can wear a set of long *u* __ __ *e r* __ __ *a* __ under all your other clothes to stay warm.

6. It was a cold day, so Megan wore a wool __ *w* __ *a t* __ __ under her jacket.

7. The legs of my brother's __ __ *n* __ __ don't fit over his boots.

8. Do you like a __ *u t* __ __ __ or a snap to fasten your skirt?

9. *P* __ *n* __ __ __ __ *s* __ make a smooth covering for legs under a skirt.

10. Jamal pulled on his sweater and zipped up his __ *a* __ *k* __ __ before going outside.

200 Words You Need to Know

FUN FILL-INS

(BONUS! Continue to fill in the blanks from the word list at the top of this page.)

zipper	boots	dry clean
iron	jeans	bleach
blouse	dryer	rinse
	detergent	

11. My __ __ *p* *p* __ __ broke, so I couldn't close up the front of my coat.

12. The only kinds of pants Diego will wear are __ __ __ *n* __ .

13. Ms. Miller, the math teacher, always wears a __ *l* __ *u* __ __ with lace trim.

14. When you go out in rain or snow, keep your feet dry by wearing __ *o* __ __ __ .

15. Some clothes can't be washed in water; you must __ __ *y* __ __ *e* *a* __ them instead.

16. *D* __ *t* __ __ *g* __ __ *t* for washing clothes comes in bottles or boxes.

17. __ __ *e* *a* __ __ helps to make clothes look whiter and brighter.

18. After washing, you must *r* __ __ *s* __ all the soap out of your clothes.

19. Then you can dry the clothes in a __ *r* *y* __ __ or hang them on a clothesline to dry.

20. If the clothes are not smooth, you can __ __ *o* __ them.

HIDDEN WORDS

Name _____

Date _____

Read the following story. Draw a line under the words from the list below when you find them in the story. Check off each word in the list as you find it. The first one is done.

skirt	shirt	sweater	rinse
jacket	socks	jeans	dry clean
pants	✔ blouse	zipper	bleach
panty hose	boots	button	dryer
underwear	shoes	iron	detergent

Shanice bought lots of clothes for school. She got a pretty <u>blouse</u> to wear with her best skirt. She found a shirt and sweater to wear with her pants and her jeans. She bought a ski jacket and wool socks to keep her warm. She needed panty hose and underwear, too. She decided to wear last year's shoes and boots.

Then Shanice washed her dirty clothes. She used bleach and detergent. After the last rinse, Shanice checked each zipper and button to be sure they weren't broken. Then she loaded the dryer. She had to iron a dress. Some clothes she couldn't wash—she had to dry clean them instead.

Now write each word you marked in the story on the lines below.

blouse _____   _____   _____

_____   _____   _____

_____   _____   _____

_____   _____   _____

_____   _____   _____

_____   _____

Name _____

Date _____

Each word in the list at the top of this page belongs in one of the categories listed below. Write each word under the category it belongs to. The first one in most categories is done for you. Check off each word in the list as you use it.

✔ skirt	underwear	boots	zipper	dry clean
✔ jacket	shirt	shoes	button	bleach
pants	socks	sweater	✔ iron	dryer
✔ panty hose	blouse	jeans	rinse	detergent

Clothing worn on the upper part of the body

jacket

_____

_____

_____

Words for fasteners

_____

_____

Words about taking care of clothes

iron

_____

_____

_____

_____

Clothing worn under all outer clothing

panty hose

_____

Clothing worn on the lower part of the body

skirt

_____

_____

_____

_____

_____

_____

BONUS! Draw a line from each clothing word to its place on the body.

Name _____

Date _____

Fill in the boxes in the puzzle with words that fit from the word list at the top of this page. Check the words off in the list as you use them. The first letter (and sometimes another one) of each word is given. The first one is done for you.

skirt	underwear	boots	zipper	dry clean
jacket	✔ shirt	shoes	button	bleach
pants	socks	sweater	iron	dryer
panty hose	blouse	jeans	rinse	detergent

BONUS! The puzzle has a secret silly sentence. It reads from the top of the puzzle down. Write the puzzle's secret silly sentence here: .

_____

                 200 Words You Need to Know

Name _____

Date _____

A word (or two together) is missing from each sentence. Choose a word (or two together) from the list that makes sense and write it in the blank for each sentence. Check off each word in the list as you use it. The first one is done.

1. Firefighters wear high rubber ____*boots*____ .   skirt

2. First wash your clothes, and then _____ them.   jacket

3. Pull up the _____ on your boot.   pants

4. A long time ago, women never wore _____ .   panty hose

5. Tube _____ go up to your knees.   underwear

6. The cheerleader wore a short _____ with pleats.   shirt

7. _____ are a kind of pants.   socks

8. Leave the clothes in the _____ for thirty minutes.   blouse

9. Ramon sewed the missing _____ onto his shirt.   ✔ boots

10. She wore a frilly _____ under her sweater.   shoes

11. Men wear a _____ under a suit jacket.   sweater

12. _____ _____ are a kind of stocking.   jeans

13. Use _____ to make your clothes whiter.   zipper

14. The baby wore a fuzzy _____ instead of a jacket.   button

BONUS! If you have filled in all the blanks above, keep going and fill in these blanks, too.   iron

15. When your clothes are wrinkled, _____ them.   rinse

16. A rain _____ keeps your upper body dry.   dry clean

17. Don't wash that coat; _____ _____ it instead.   bleach

18. It's not easy to walk in _____ with high heels.   dryer

19. The rain soaked all his clothes, right through to his   detergent

    _____ .

20. Dad uses liquid _____ to wash the clothes.

200 Words You Need to Know

DAFFY DEFINITIONS

Choose the correct definition for each word. Circle the letter in front of the definition you choose.

1. jacket
   - (a) short coat
   - (b) loud noise
   - (c) soft pudding

2. zipper
   - (a) small, round fastener
   - (b) fastener with teeth and a slide
   - (c) fastener with a hook and eye

3. panty hose
   - (a) rubber watering tube
   - (b) bathing suit
   - (c) one-piece stockings

4. iron
   - (a) to press clothes
   - (b) to make angry
   - (c) to clean clothes

5. button
   - (a) small, round fastener
   - (b) fastener with teeth and a slide
   - (c) fastener with a hook and eye

6. rinse
   - (a) to stretch out
   - (b) to dry
   - (c) to wash off with clear water

7. dry clean
   - (a) to wash with water
   - (b) to clean without water
   - (c) to get dirty

8. bleach
   - (a) to make darker
   - (b) to make whiter or brighter
   - (c) to hang out to dry

9. dryer
   - (a) machine to wash clothes
   - (b) machine to iron clothes
   - (c) machine to dry clothes

10. detergent
    - (a) powder or liquid used to wash clothes
    - (b) liquid used to color clothes
    - (c) powder used to get clothes dirty

Name _____

Date _____

(BONUS! Continue to circle the correct definition for each word.)

11. skirt
    (a) short coat
    (b) garment with no legs that hangs from the waist
    (c) clothing for the upper body

12. pants
    (a) clothing with two legs
    (b) garment with no legs that hangs from the waist
    (c) pieces of something

13. underwear
    (a) clothing you wear on your head
    (b) warm coat for winter
    (c) clothing you wear beneath other clothes

14. shirt
    (a) something you wear on your feet
    (b) clothing for the upper body
    (c) warm season of the year

15. socks
    (a) things to keep your hands warm
    (b) things to keep your head warm
    (c) things to keep your feet warm

16. blouse
    (a) sad story
    (b) covering for the legs
    (c) clothing for the upper body

17. boots
    (a) covering for the feet and lower legs
    (b) vegetable soup
    (c) something to keep the hands warm

18. shoes
    (a) something you wear on your head
    (b) something you wear on your feet
    (c) a furry pet animal

19. sweater
    (a) clothing to help keep you warm
    (b) clothing to go swimming in
    (c) clothing to wear on your lower body

20. jeans
    (a) a kind of jacket
    (b) a kind of shirt
    (c) a kind of pants

200 Words You Need to Know

Choose an ending that makes sense for each sentence. Circle the letter in front of the ending you choose. The vocabulary word or words in each sentence are underlined.

1. Vanessa bought a new <u>skirt</u>
   (a) to wear to bed.
   (b) at the hardware store.
   (c) to wear to the dance.

2. My mother always tells me to wear a <u>jacket</u>
   (a) when it's cool outside.
   (b) in the shower.
   (c) under my shoes.

3. The <u>zipper</u> was invented to
   (a) improve people's diets.
   (b) take the place of buttons.
   (c) keep feet warm.

4. When you wear <u>pants</u>,
   (a) your head is covered.
   (b) your legs are covered.
   (c) your arms are covered.

5. Girls wear <u>panty hose</u>
   (a) under their sweaters.
   (b) on their hands.
   (c) on their legs.

6. Use a warm <u>iron</u>
   (a) to press out the wrinkles.
   (b) to clean your skirt.
   (c) to wash the dishes.

7. <u>Underwear</u> goes on
   (a) under your other clothes.
   (b) over your jacket.
   (c) over your boots.

8. Lorenzo's button-down <u>shirt</u>
   (a) was served for dinner.
   (b) read a book.
   (c) went well with his pants.

9. I could see his bright green <u>socks</u>
   (a) under his shirt.
   (b) below his pants.
   (c) around his neck.

10. Rosa's rose-colored <u>blouse</u>
    (a) played basketball well.
    (b) was very pretty.
    (c) fed the dog every afternoon.

Name _____

Date _____

(BONUS! Continue to choose an ending that makes sense for each sentence.)

11. I bought a pair of cowboy <u>boots</u>
    (a) so I could swim faster.
    (b) for my pet hamster.
    (c) to go with my denim jeans.

12. Sew some new <u>buttons</u>
    (a) onto your old coat.
    (b) onto your oven.
    (c) onto your bathtub.

13. Let's take off our <u>shoes</u> so
    (a) we can hear better.
    (b) our hands will be bare.
    (c) our feet will be bare.

14. Do you think this yellow <u>sweater</u>
    (a) is easy to drive?
    (b) can be washed in water?
    (c) can play the piano?

15. Wash, <u>rinse</u>, and spin are
    (a) three steps in baking a cake.
    (b) three things a washing machine does.
    (c) three rules of baseball.

16. Be sure to <u>dry clean</u>
    (a) your wool coat.
    (b) the apple tree.
    (c) the river.

17. Healy poured <u>bleach</u> into
    (a) the washing machine.
    (b) the closet.
    (c) her teacher's desk drawer.

18. My brother uses the <u>dryer</u>
    (a) to wash his clothes.
    (b) to iron his clothes.
    (c) to dry his clothes.

19. Lashonda's <u>jeans</u> are worn-out because
    (a) they are new.
    (b) they are old.
    (c) they are blue.

20. I bought a big box of <u>detergent</u>
    (a) to cook for supper.
    (b) to wear to church.
    (c) for washing my clothes.

Unit 5

WEATHER WORDS

Read each word below and its definition. Rewrite each word in the blanks next to its definition.

1. snow   soft white frozen flakes; or, to fall as snow   _ _ _ [w]

2. drizzle   very light rain; or, to rain gently and steadily   _ _ [i] _ _ _ _

3. cloud   a filmy or puffy mass that seems to float in the air   _ [l] _ _ _

4. flood   great flow of water; or, to overflow or cover with water   _ [l] _ _ _

5. tornado   violent windstorm with a dark column reaching to the ground   [t] _ _ _ _ _ _

6. heat   warmth, the state of being hot; or, to make hot or warm   [h] _ _ _

7. sleet   frozen or partly frozen rain; or, to fall as sleet   _ _ [e] _ _ _

8. wind   air moving along the earth   [w] _ _ _

9. freeze   to harden into ice   _ _ [e] _ _ _

10. temperature   amount of warmth or coldness   _ _ _ _ _ _ _ [a] _ _ _ _

11. drought   period of dry weather, with very little or no rain   _ _ _ _ _ _ [t]

12. lightning   electric flash in the sky   _ _ _ [h] _ _ _ _ _

13. forecast   statement of what is going to happen; or to make a forecast   _ _ _ [e] _ _ _ _

14. hurricane   violent storm with very high winds and heavy rain   _ _ _ [r] _ _ _ _ _

15. cold   lack of heat or warmth; or, not warm   [c] _ _ _

16. thunder   loud noise after lightning; or, to make thunder   _ [h] _ _ _ _ _

17. rain   water that falls from clouds to the earth; or, to fall as rain   _ [a] _ _

18. sunny   full of sunlight   _ _ [n] _ _

19. fog   cloud of tiny water drops close to the ground; or, to cover with fog   _ _ [g]

20. ice   frozen water; or, to cover with ice   _ _ [e]

BONUS! The boxed letters spell out a sentence. What does it say? (Write it out here if you want:)

FUN FILL-INS

Name _____

Date _____

Each sentence below has a word missing. Fill in each blank with a word that makes sense from the list at the top of this page. Check off each word in the list as you use it.

snow	flood	wind
drizzle	thunder	freeze
sleet	cloud	temperature
	heat	

1. The strong __ __ __ *d* blew off my hat.

2. The loud clap of *t* __ __ *n* *d* __ __ came right after the lightning.

3. The __ *e* __ __ wave lasted for two weeks last summer.

4. A foot of __ *n* __ __ fell overnight and covered the steps.

5. The *t* __ __ *p* __ *r* *a* __ __ __ *e* was only 40°, so we all wore jackets.

6. The __ __ *o* *o* __ washed right through my aunt's yard.

7. A cold and steady __ *r* __ __ *z* *l* __ fell all day.

8. I hope the pond will *f* __ *e* __ __ __ soon so we can go ice skating.

9. The sun was hidden behind a huge __ *l* __ *u* __ .

10. The icy __ *l* __ __ *t* covered all the trees and bushes.

     200 Words You Need to Know

Name _____

Date _____

(BONUS! Continue to fill in the blanks from the word list at the top of this page.)

drought	hurricane	tornado
lightning	cold	fog
forecast	sunny	ice
	rain	

11. A _t_ _ _r_ _ _a_ _ _ will smash everything in its path.

12. Each tropical storm called a _ _u_ _r_ _ _i_ _ _ _n_ _e_ is given a boy's or a girl's name.

13. Never stand under a tree during a thunder and _l_ _ _g_ _h_ _ _n_ _ _ _ storm.

14. When it gets _ _ _ _d_ in our apartment, my mother turns on the heat.

15. My little sister wears rubber boots when she walks to school in the _ _a_ _ _ .

16. The weather _f_ _ _r_ _e_ _ _ _s_ _ says it will be warm and sunny all day.

17. Monday started out rainy but ended up _ _u_ _n_ _ _ .

18. Put _ _ _e_ cubes in your soda to make it colder.

19. Because of the _ _r_ _o_ _ _ _h_ _ , the crops couldn't grow.

20. The _ _o_ _ was very thick, so we couldn't see far.

HIDDEN WORDS

Name _____

Date _____

Read the following story. Draw a line under the words from the list below when you find them in the story. Check off each word in the list as you find it. The first one is done.

snow	heat	drought	thunder
✔ drizzle	sleet	lightning	rain
clouds	wind	forecast	sunny
flood	freeze	hurricane	fog
tornado	temperature	cold	ice

Weather changes by the season. In the spring, it may <u>drizzle</u> one day and be sunny the next day. Sometimes there's too much rain, and it causes a flood. Temperature changes can create fog. Summer brings heat and puffy clouds, plus thunder and lightning storms. But sometimes there's too little rain, which causes drought. A hurricane or tornado can happen late in the summer or fall. In the winter, water can freeze into ice. Snow or sleet falls, and a cold wind blows. The weather forecast tells us when to expect these changes—but the forecast isn't always right!

Now write each word you marked in the story on the lines below. (You may have marked two words twice—just write each one once here.)

drizzle _____   _____   _____

_____   _____   _____

_____   _____   _____

_____   _____   _____

_____   _____   _____

_____   _____   _____

_____   _____

Name _____

Date _____

Each word in the list at the top of this page belongs in one of the categories listed below. Write each word under the category it belongs to. The first one in each category is done for you. Check off each word in the list as you use it.

✔ snow   ✔ tornado   freeze   forecast   rain

✔ drizzle   heat   temperature   hurricane   sunny

  cloud   sleet   drought   cold   fog

✔ flood   wind   lightning   thunder   ice

Begins with a letter between *A* and *D*

drizzle

_____

_____

_____

Begins with a letter between *E* and *H*

flood

_____

_____

_____

_____

_____

Begins with a letter between *I* and *S*

snow

_____

_____

_____

_____

_____

Begins with a letter between *T* and *Z*

tornado

_____

_____

_____

Fill in the boxes in the puzzle with words that fit from the word list at the top of this page. Check the words off in the list as you use them. The first letter (and sometimes another one) of each word is given. The first one is done for you.

snow	tornado	freeze	forecast	rain
drizzle	✔heat	temperature	hurricane	sunny
cloud	sleet	drought	cold	fog
flood	wind	lightning	thunder	ice

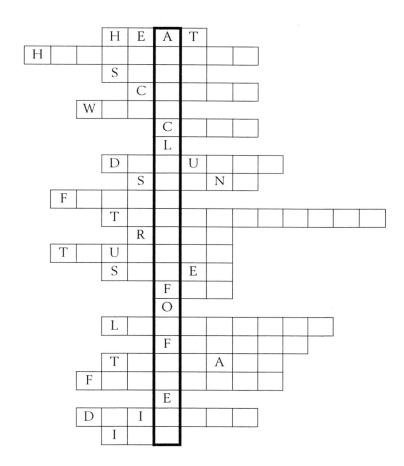

BONUS! The puzzle has a secret silly sentence. It reads from the top of the puzzle down. Write the puzzle's secret silly sentence here:

_____

200 Words You Need to Know

WHAT'S MISSING?

Name _____

Date _____

A word is missing from each sentence. Choose a word from the list that makes sense and write it in the blank for each sentence. Check off each word in the list as you use it. The first one is done.

1. Did you hear that ____*thunder*____ ?

2. A strong _____ was blowing.

3. Is the _____ hard enough to skate on?

4. A bolt of _____ lit up the sky.

5. The _____ fell in large fluffy flakes.

6. Our pond dried up during the _____ .

7. The heavy _____ made big puddles.

8. Rain fell from the dark _____ overhead.

9. Please _____ the water to make ice cubes.

10. I only go to the beach on _____ days.

11. You can see the funnel of a _____ from miles away.

12. We checked the _____ so we'd know what weather to expect.

13. Our barn floated away in the _____ .

14. The _____ in the desert is hot during the day and cold at night.

BONUS! If you have filled in all the blanks above, keep going and fill in these blanks, too.

15. A _____ brings high winds and heavy rain.

16. Frozen rain is called _____ .

17. Do you think it would be _____ inside an igloo?

18. You can't see far in heavy _____ .

19. Steady, gentle rain is called _____ .

20. I could feel the _____ of the sun through my jacket.

snow

drizzle

cloud

flood

tornado

heat

sleet

wind

freeze

temperature

drought

lightning

forecast

hurricane

cold

✔ thunder

rain

sunny

fog

ice

200 Words You Need to Know

Name _____

Date _____

Choose the correct definition for each word. Circle the letter in front of the definition you choose.

1. snow
   - (a) gentle rain
   - (b) soft white flakes
   - (c) not fast

2. drizzle
   - (a) very light rain
   - (b) large brown bear
   - (c) high winds

3. sleet
   - (a) strong sunlight
   - (b) frozen rain
   - (c) bed covering

4. flood
   - (a) frozen water
   - (b) flash of light
   - (c) great flow of water

5. wind
   - (a) soft rain
   - (b) cold temperature
   - (c) moving air

6. freeze
   - (a) harden into ice
   - (b) fall asleep
   - (c) soak up sun

7. temperature
   - (a) state of mind
   - (b) amount of warmth or coldness
   - (c) violent storm

8. lightning
   - (a) flash of light
   - (b) sunlight
   - (c) lightbulb

9. forecast
   - (a) statement of what will happen
   - (b) woods
   - (c) story about the past

10. sunny
    - (a) covered by clouds
    - (b) a day of the week
    - (c) full of sunlight

Name _____

Date _____

(BONUS! Continue to circle the correct definition for each word.)

11. cloud
   - (a) large group of people
   - (b) puffy mass in the air
   - (c) cold rain

12. tornado
   - (a) violent windstorm
   - (b) soft white flakes
   - (c) period of very dry weather

13. heat
   - (a) extreme cold
   - (b) state of being warm
   - (c) frozen rain

14. drought
   - (a) period of heavy rain
   - (b) period of extreme heat
   - (c) period of very dry weather

15. hurricane
   - (a) mob of people
   - (b) cloud of tiny water drops
   - (c) violent wind and rain storm

16. cold
   - (a) state of being warm
   - (b) lack of heat
   - (c) young horse

17. thunder
   - (a) loud noise in the sky
   - (b) loud music
   - (c) flash of light in the sky

18. rain
   - (a) water that falls from clouds
   - (b) soft white frozen flakes
   - (c) extreme anger

19. fog
   - (a) green creature
   - (b) piece of wood
   - (c) cloud of tiny water drops

20. ice
   - (a) group of raindrops
   - (b) frozen water
   - (c) long-ago times

EXERCISE 8
SENTENCE SENSE

Name _____

Date _____

Choose an ending that makes sense for each sentence. Circle the letter in front of the ending you choose. The vocabulary word in each sentence is underlined.

1. The children playing in the <u>snow</u>
   (a) threw snowballs at each other.
   (b) stayed inside their homes.
   (c) wore bathing suits.

2. If there's a <u>drizzle</u> of rain,
   (a) we'll lie out in the sun.
   (b) the ground will be dry.
   (c) it will be too wet to paint the house.

3. When <u>clouds</u> fill the sky,
   (a) the day is bright and sunny.
   (b) the day is not sunny.
   (c) the moon is red.

4. During the <u>flood</u>, the river
   (a) dried up.
   (b) covered the road nearby.
   (c) stayed at a low level.

5. The <u>tornado</u> raced through town and
   (a) destroyed a lot of buildings.
   (b) washed the dirty clothes.
   (c) fixed the sidewalks.

6. <u>Sleet</u> feels
   (a) hot and wet.
   (b) warm and dry.
   (c) cold and icy.

7. The high <u>heat</u> of the day made me feel
   (a) like going swimming.
   (b) like wearing my winter coat.
   (c) very cold.

8. You need some blowing <u>wind</u>
   (a) to fly a kite.
   (b) to bake a cake.
   (c) to go to school.

9. During the winter, water will <u>freeze</u>
   (a) and become sand.
   (b) and turn red.
   (c) and become ice.

10. <u>Temperature</u> measures
    (a) how tall you are.
    (b) how warm or cold it is.
    (c) how long the day is.

59   *200 Words You Need to Know*

(BONUS! Continue to choose an ending that makes sense for each sentence.)

11. During a <u>drought</u>, there's not enough
    (a) sun.
    (b) clouds.
    (c) rain.

12. In the middle of the storm, I saw a <u>lightning</u> bolt
    (a) in my bathtub.
    (b) in the sky.
    (c) in my dog's supper dish.

13. The weather <u>forecast</u>
    (a) said it would rain yesterday.
    (b) said it would rain tomorrow.
    (c) tasted good.

14. When the <u>hurricane</u> came,
    (a) we enjoyed the bright sun.
    (b) we shook hands with it.
    (c) many trees blew over.

15. My toes got <u>cold</u> when I
    (a) went barefoot in the snow.
    (b) soaked them in hot water.
    (c) kept them warm with wool socks.

16. You often hear <u>thunder</u>
    (a) after you see lightning.
    (b) on a bright, sunny day.
    (c) when you eat ice cream.

17. If you go out in the <u>rain</u> with no umbrella or raincoat,
    (a) you'll stay dry.
    (b) you'll turn green.
    (c) you'll get wet.

18. On a <u>sunny</u> day,
    (a) it's dark and cloudy.
    (b) there's lots of sunshine.
    (c) it rains all day.

19. Thick <u>fog</u>
    (a) means the air is very clear.
    (b) is hard to see through.
    (c) is served often for lunch.

20. <u>Ice</u> is
    (a) hard and cold.
    (b) soft and warm.
    (c) dry and hot.

Unit 6
ENTERTAINMENT WORDS

EXERCISE 1
ENTERTAINMENT WORD SENSE

Name _____

Date _____

Read each word below and its definition. Rewrite each word in the blanks next to its definition.

1. stereo — device with two or more speakers that plays sound recordings — [s] _ _ _ _ _

2. cassette — small plastic tape container — _ _ _ _ [e] _ _ _

3. game — way to play; contest with rules — _ _ _ [e]

4. album — long-playing CD; also, a book with blank pages — [a] _ _ _ _

5. movie — motion picture — [m] _ _ _ _

6. video — having to do with a television picture; or, the TV picture itself — _ _ _ _ [o]

7. VCR — video cassette recorder, a device that plays and records videotapes — [V] _ _

8. radio — device for sending sound by electric waves — _ _ _ [i] _

9. cable — a bundle of wires that carries TV signals, electricity, etc. — _ _ _ _ [e]

10. tape — ribbon of plastic for recording sounds; or, to record on tape — _ [a] _ _

11. computer — electronic machine that stores and processes information — _ _ _ _ _ [t] _ _

12. sport — game in which you're physically active — _ _ _ _ [t]

13. hobby — activity you do regularly in your spare time because you enjoy it — [h] _ _ _ _

14. concert — public performance of music — _ _ _ _ [e] _ _

15. CD — compact disk with recorded sound and/or information — [C] _

16. cinema — movie theater — _ [i] _ _ _ _

17. dance — to move in time to music; also, a party where you dance — _ _ [n] _ _

18. television — device that shows pictures and plays sounds sent by electric waves; TV — _ _ _ [e] _ _ _ _ _ _

19. admission — allowing someone to enter a place; also, fee paid to enter — _ _ [m] _ _ _ _ _

20. theater — place where movies are shown or plays are staged — _ _ _ [a] _ _ _

BONUS! The boxed letters spell out a sentence. What does it say? (Write it out here if you want:)

200 Words You Need to Know

Name _____

Date _____

Each sentence below has a word (or two words together) missing. Fill in each blank with a word that makes sense from the list at the top of this page. Check off each word in the list as you use it.

stereo	album	radio
cassette	movie	cable
game	video	tape
	VCR	

1. I rented a video to play at home on my __ __ *R* .

2. Before television, kids listened to many different __ __ *d i* __ shows.

3. I bought my brother Ali the new CD *a* __ __ __ *m* he wanted for his birthday.

4. Sara wears a headset and listens to a __ __ *s s* __ __ *t* __ while she jogs.

5. Now that we have __ __ *b* __ *e* TV, we have many channels to choose from.

6. My cousin Dan always seems to be watching a rock __ __ *d e* __ on his television.

7. Hurry up, or we'll be late and miss the beginning of the *m* __ *v* __ __ .

8. Riva wants a __ *t* __ __ __ *o* so she can play her record albums whenever she wants.

9. Don't you wish you had a __ __ *P* __ of that new song?

10. The children were playing a __ *a* __ __ that went on for hours.

200 Words You Need to Know

Name _____

Date _____

(BONUS! Continue to fill in the blanks from the word list at the top of this page.)

computer   concert   television
sport   CD   admission
hobby   cinema   theater
                  dance

11. Devon likes to play games on his __ __ *m* __ __ *t* __ __ at home.

12. Did you hear that song on tape or on a __ __ ?

13. The drama club staged a play at a local *t* __ __ __ __ *e* __ .

14. What is your favorite *s* __ __ *r* __ ?

15. My sister's __ __ *b* __ *y* is raising ants. Isn't that strange?

16. *Sesame Street* is still a very popular *t* __ *l* __ *v* __ __ *i* *o* __ show for children.

17. The __ *i* *n* __ __ __ at the shopping mall shows five different movies at once.

18. The school band gave a *c* __ __ *c* __ __ __ for students, parents, and teachers.

19. The student council hired a live band to play at the __ __ *n* *c* __ on Saturday night.

20. How much is the *a* *d* __ __ *s* *s* __ __ __ fee to get into that amusement park?

Read the following story. Draw a line under the words from the list below when you find them in the story. Check off each word in the list as you find it. The first one is done.

stereo	video	computer	cinema
cassette	VCR	sports	dance
games	radio	✔ hobby	television
album	cable	concert	admission
movie	tape	CD	theater

    I do many things to entertain myself. At home, I work on my <u>hobby</u> by putting stamps in my album. I may watch a sports event on cable television or watch a video on the VCR. I enjoy playing games on my computer, too. I often listen to a CD on the stereo. Sometimes I tape a song from the radio onto a cassette.

    When I'm not at home, I like to see a movie at the local theater, which is called Mall Cinema. Sometimes I use a free pass for admission. I enjoy live music at a dance or a concert. Entertainment is relaxing and fun for me.

Now write each word you marked in the story on the lines below.

hobby _____   _____   _____

_____   _____   _____

_____   _____   _____

_____   _____   _____

_____   _____   _____

_____   _____

 200 Words You Need to Know

Name _____

Date _____

Each word in the list at the top of this page belongs in one of the categories listed below. Write each word under the category it belongs to. A few are done for you. Check off each word in the list as you use it.

✔ stereo	✔ movie	cable	hobby	✔ dance
cassette	video	tape	concert	television
game	VCR	computer	CD	admission
album	radio	sport	cinema	theater

Words related to listening to music

stereo

_____

_____

_____

_____

_____

Words related to seeing something on a screen

movie

_____

_____

_____

_____

_____

_____

Word related to something you play or do for fun

dance

_____

_____

_____

Word related to entrance fees

_____

Powerful machine you use for fun and study

_____

Name _____

Date _____

Fill in the boxes in the puzzle with words that fit from the word list at the top of this page. Check the words off in the list as you use them. The first letter (and sometimes another one) of each word is given. The first one is done for you.

stereo	movie	cable	hobby	dance
cassette	✔ video	tape	concert	television
game	VCR	computer	CD	admission
album	radio	sport	cinema	theater

BONUS! The puzzle has a secret silly sentence. It reads from the top of the puzzle down. Write the puzzle's secret silly sentence here:

_____

200 Words You Need to Know

EXERCISE 6
WHAT'S MISSING?

Name _____

Date _____

A word is missing from each sentence. Choose a word from the list that makes sense and write it in the blank for each sentence. Check off each word in the list as you use it. The first one is done.

1. Stamp collecting is a popular ___*hobby*___ .

2. TV is the short way to say _____ .

3. A _____ has two or more speakers.

4. It's great to see your favorite band in a live _____ .

5. You go to a cinema to see a _____ .

6. A tape comes in a small plastic box called a _____ .

7. You go to a _____ to see a movie or a stage play.

8. Which _____ games do you like to play?

9. I love to play a _____ of soccer.

10. Another word for *movie theater* is _____ .

11. You can use a _____ to get information from all over the world.

12. You have a choice of many different channels if you have

    _____ TV in your home.

13. Does that amusement park charge an _____ fee?

14. A _____ plays movies that are recorded on a cassette.

BONUS! If you have filled in all the blanks above, keep going and fill in these blanks, too.

15. Do you like to _____ ?

16. An _____ is a long-playing CD.

17. You play a compact disk on a _____ player.

18. A cassette is a container for a _____ .

19. You can listen to either AM or FM _____ stations.

20. Which _____ do you like best, football or soccer?

stereo

cassette

game

album

movie

video

VCR

radio

cable

tape

computer

sport

✔ hobby

concert

CD

cinema

dance

television

admission

theater

200 Words You Need to Know

DAFFY DEFINITIONS

Name _____

Date _____

Choose the correct definition for each word. Circle the letter in front of the definition you choose.

1. stereo
   - (a) television
   - (b) device that plays recordings
   - (c) mixing bowl

2. cassette
   - (a) long-playing CD
   - (b) plastic tape container
   - (c) live concert

3. movie
   - (a) motion picture
   - (b) soft drink
   - (c) CD player

4. video
   - (a) small yellow bird
   - (b) cowboys' sport
   - (c) television picture

5. hobby
   - (a) hallway
   - (b) boy's name
   - (c) spare-time activity

6. concert
   - (a) long speech
   - (b) public performance of music
   - (c) motion picture

7. CD
   - (a) compact disk
   - (b) cassette drive
   - (c) computer dance

8. cinema
   - (a) game played with a round ball
   - (b) spice used in cakes
   - (c) movie theater

9. television
   - (a) tape recorder
   - (b) CD player
   - (c) TV

10. admission
    - (a) cassette
    - (b) fee paid to enter a place
    - (c) video game

Name _____

Date _____

(BONUS! Continue to circle the correct definition for each word.)

11. game
    (a) something fun to play
    (b) violent storm
    (c) motion picture

12. album
    (a) boring homework
    (b) bunny rabbit
    (c) long-playing CD

13. VCR
    (a) variable control remote
    (b) video cassette recorder
    (c) very comic radio

14. cable
    (a) high tower
    (b) wires carrying TV signals
    (c) piece of furniture

15. tape
    (a) round disk
    (b) short story
    (c) ribbon for recording

16. computer
    (a) VCR
    (b) radio
    (c) powerful information machine

17. sport
    (a) physical game
    (b) activity you do while you sleep
    (c) walking stick

18. dance
    (a) cook a meal
    (b) move in time to music
    (c) dig in the garden

19. theater
    (a) place to play a sport
    (b) television set
    (c) place to see a movie

20. radio
    (a) something you listen to
    (b) something you watch videos on
    (c) something you play

SENTENCE SENSE

Name _____

Date _____

Choose an ending that makes sense for each sentence. Circle the letter in front of the ending you choose. The vocabulary word or words in each sentence are underlined.

1. Leon played a CD on the <u>stereo</u> and
   (a) listened to the music.
   (b) watched the movie it showed.
   (c) baked it in the oven.

2. My sister always has a <u>cassette</u> with her
   (a) to put in the washing machine.
   (b) that she rides to school.
   (c) to listen to.

3. In gym class, we played a <u>game</u>
   (a) flying on the ceiling.
   (b) of popcorn.
   (c) of volleyball.

4. A stamp <u>album</u> is
   (a) a hole in the ground.
   (b) a book to keep stamps in.
   (c) a funny movie.

5. Our teacher showed a <u>movie</u> that was
   (a) fun to watch.
   (b) hard to read.
   (c) 300 pages long.

6. I rented a <u>video</u>
   (a) to read at home.
   (b) to watch last night.
   (c) to cook for supper.

7. A <u>VCR</u> plays
   (a) the piano.
   (b) videotapes on a TV screen.
   (c) basketball.

8. Turn on the <u>radio</u> and
   (a) listen to the news.
   (b) watch the picture it shows.
   (c) dry your hair with it.

9. The <u>cable</u> repair person arrived to
   (a) baby-sit.
   (b) fix the washing machine.
   (c) fix the picture on our TV.

10. I bought a blank <u>tape</u>
    (a) to read at the library.
    (b) to put in the cake mix.
    (c) to record my favorite album.

(BONUS! Continue to choose an ending that makes sense for each sentence.)

11. I turned on my <u>computer</u>
    (a) to light up the kitchen.
    (b) to play a game.
    (c) to make the coffee.

12. Some popular <u>sports</u> are
    (a) tennis, swimming, and baseball.
    (b) chopping wood.
    (c) being sick and staying in bed.

13. A <u>hobby</u> is something you do
    (a) that you don't like.
    (b) because you enjoy it.
    (c) when you're asleep.

14. Julio and Mike went to the <u>concert</u>
    (a) to read the book.
    (b) to see the movie.
    (c) to hear the music.

15. Put the <u>CD</u>
    (a) in the spaghetti sauce.
    (b) in the VCR and watch it.
    (c) in the stereo and play it.

16. The new <u>cinema</u>
    (a) shows six movies at once.
    (b) asked Irene for a date.
    (c) delivered the mail.

17. At a <u>dance</u>, you
    (a) move in time to music.
    (b) cook vegetables.
    (c) must sit down and not move.

18. Our new color <u>television</u>
    (a) has four wheels and an engine.
    (b) is fun to watch.
    (c) cleans the house well.

19. Racquel and Malcolm paid an <u>admission</u> fee
    (a) to get out of the swimming pool.
    (b) to get into the boat show.
    (c) to the rabbit.

20. At a <u>theater,</u> you
    (a) buy milk and cheese.
    (b) borrow library books.
    (c) watch movies.

Unit 7

CAR WORDS

CAR WORD SENSE

Name _____

Date _____

Read each word below and its definition. Rewrite each word in the blanks next to its definition.

1. license — card showing that you are legally allowed to drive — _ _ [c] _ _ _ _

2. mph — miles per hour; a measure of speed — _ _ [h]

3. seat belt — strap to hold you safely in your seat — _ _ [a] _ _ _ _ _

4. coolant — a liquid that cools the engine — _ _ _ _ _ [n] _

5. register — to record your ownership of a car legally and officially — _ _ _ [g] _ _ _ _

6. fuel — material, like gas, that is burned in an engine to produce power — _ _ [e] _

7. engine — machine that uses energy to make a car go — _ _ _ _ _ [e]

8. ignition — system for starting a car's engine — _ _ [n] _ _ _ _ _

9. gas — gasoline, the liquid fuel most often used to make a car's engine go — [g] _ _

10. oil — greasy liquid used on the moving parts of an engine — _ [i] _

11. windshield — glass or plastic screen in front of people in a car — _ _ [n] _ _ _ _ _ _

12. brakes — devices that slow down or stop a car — _ _ _ _ [e] _

13. hood — movable metal cover over a car's engine — _ [o] _ _

14. tire — band of rubber around a wheel — _ [i] _ _

15. headlight — bright light on the front of a car — _ _ _ _ _ _ _ [l] _

16. automobile — car; motor vehicle — _ _ _ _ [o] _ _ _ _ _

17. muffler — device that reduces engine noise — _ _ [f] _ _ _ _

18. toll — money you must pay to use a highway, bridge, or tunnel — [t] _ _ _

19. speed limit — fastest speed that is allowed — _ _ _ [e] _ _ _ _ _ _

20. inspection — checking of a car to be sure it is in good condition — _ [n] _ _ _ _ _ _ _ _

BONUS! The boxed letters spell out a sentence. What does it say? (Write it out here if you want:)

200 Words You Need to Know

Each sentence below has a word (or two words together) missing. Fill in each blank with a word that makes sense from the list at the top of this page. Check off each word in the list as you use it.

license	coolant	ignition
mph	register	gas
seat belt	fuel	oil
	engine	

1. Put your key into the __ _g_ _n_ __ __ _i_ __ __ switch and turn it to start the engine.

2. What kind of __ __ __ _l_ does that car use—gas or diesel?

3. The _e_ __ _g_ __ __ __ ran smoothly after it was tuned up.

4. Franco got his driver's __ _i_ _c_ __ __ __ __ as soon as he turned 16 years old.

5. __ _i_ __ coats the engine's moving parts that rub together so they won't stick.

6. My car stopped running when it ran out of __ _a_ __ .

7. I made sure I did not drive faster than the posted speed limit of 45 __ _p_ __ .

8. You must _r_ __ __ _i_ _s_ __ __ __ a car with your state before you can legally drive it.

9. The engine overheated because the __ _o_ __ __ __ _n_ __ was gone.

10. In many states, the law says everyone riding in a car must wear a

_s_ __ __ __   _b_ __ __ __ .

200 Words You Need to Know

Name _____

Date _____

(BONUS! Continue to fill in the blanks from the word list at the top of this page.)

windshield   tire   toll
brakes   headlight   speed limit
hood   automobile   inspection
                muffler

11. How do you open the _h_ __ __ __ of your car?

12. After I drove over a broken bottle, my __ __ _r_ __ went flat.

13. An engine sounds loud if the __ _u_ _f_ __ _l_ __ __ has a hole in it.

14. The sign said, "Last Exit Before __ __ __ _l_ ."

15. The police officer stopped Nick because he was driving much faster than the

    __ _p_ __ _e_ __ __ __ _m_ __ _t_ .

16. A car has a right and a left _h_ __ __ _d_ _l_ __ _g_ __ __ to light up the road at night.

17. A safe car must have good __ _r_ __ _k_ __ __ .

18. In many states, your car must pass _i_ __ _s_ __ __ _c_ _t_ __ __ __ once or twice a year.

19. My older brother went to work in an __ _u_ _t_ __ _m_ __ _b_ __ __ __ factory after he finished high school.

20. Use the wipers to keep the _w_ __ __ _d_ _s_ __ _i_ _e_ __ __ clear when it's raining.

Read the following story. Draw a line under the words from the list below when you find them in the story. Check off each word in the list as you find it. The first one is done.

✔ license	fuel	windshield	automobile
mph	engine	brakes	muffler
seat belt	ignition	hood	toll
coolant	gas	tire	speed limit
register	oil	headlight	inspection

    After Kim got her driver's <u>license</u>, she bought an automobile. First she went to register the car. During inspection, important parts of the car were checked—the muffler, the brakes, each headlight, each tire, and each seat belt. Kim knew the ignition worked because the engine started right up.

    Then she drove to a gas station for fuel. She raised the hood and checked the oil level and the coolant. She also cleaned the windshield. Then she drove her car home. On the way, she paid a toll and was careful to stay below the speed limit of 40 mph.

Now write each word you marked in the story on the lines below.

license
_____   _____   _____

_____   _____   _____

_____   _____   _____

_____   _____   _____

_____   _____   _____

_____   _____   _____

_____   _____

LUCKY LISTS

Name _____

Date _____

Each word in the list at the top of this page belongs in one of the categories listed below. Write each word under the category it belongs to. Some are done for you. Check off each word in the list as you use it.

✔ license	register	gas	hood	muffler
✔ mph	fuel	oil	tire	toll
✔ seat belt	engine	windshield	headlight	speed limit
coolant	ignition	brakes	automobile	inspection

Parts of a car

_seat belt_____

_____

_____

_____

_____

_____

_____

_____

Liquids used in a car's engine

_____

_____

_____

_____

Words related to road signs and highways

_mph_____

_____

_____

BONUS! Draw a line from each car-part word you listed to the place on the car where you would find the part.

Words related to legally owning and driving a car

_license_____

_____

_____

_____

Another word for car

_____

200 Words You Need to Know

PUZZLE TIME

Name _____

Date _____

Fill in the boxes in the puzzle with words that fit from the word list at the top of this page. Check the words off in the list as you use them. The first letter (and sometimes another one) of each word is given. The first one is done for you.

license	register	gas	hood	muffler
mph	fuel	oil	tire	toll
seat belt	engine	windshield	headlight	speed limit
coolant	✔ ignition	brakes	automobile	inspection

BONUS! The puzzle has a secret silly sentence. It reads from the top of the puzzle down. Write the puzzle's secret silly sentence here:

_____

200 Words You Need to Know

WHAT'S MISSING?

A word (or two or together) is missing from each sentence. Choose a word (or two together) from the list that makes sense and write it in the blank for each sentence. Check off each word in the list as you use it. The first one is done.

1. ___*Gas*___ is a short way to say *gasoline*.

2. Open the hood so we can see the _____ .

3. The speed limit was 35 _____ .

4. Can you change a flat _____ ?

5. _____ is another word for *car*.

6. Use the_____ to stop the car.

7. Always wear your _____ _____ .

8. You must pay a _____ of 50 cents to cross that bridge.

9. Keep the _____ clean so you can see through it clearly.

10. The engine was very noisy without its _____ .

11. The _____ most often used in cars is gas.

12. The _____ _____ was 55 mph.

13. The car's engine is under the _____ .

14. Change your engine _____ often.

BONUS! If you have filled in all the blanks above, keep going and fill in these blanks, too.

15. The _____ starts the engine.

16. You need each _____ to light up all of the road at night.

17. Be sure to _____ your car with your state each year.

18. Don't drive without a driver's _____ .

19. An _____ checks the condition of your car.

20. _____ keeps your car's engine from running too hot and stopping.

license

mph

seat belt

coolant

register

fuel

engine

ignition

✔ gas

oil

windshield

brakes

hood

tire

headlight

automobile

muffler

toll

speed limit

inspection

80   *200 Words You Need to Know*

DAFFY DEFINITIONS

Choose the correct definition for each word. Circle the letter in front of the definition you choose.

1. license
   - (a) card showing you can drive
   - (b) electric light
   - (c) speed limit

2. mph
   - (a) miles per hour
   - (b) money paid here
   - (c) muffler pipe hole

3. register
   - (a) to wash a car
   - (b) to record ownership of a car
   - (c) to start a car

4. engine
   - (a) a device that stops a car
   - (b) machine that makes a car go
   - (c) liquid that makes a car go

5. gas
   - (a) animal feed
   - (b) brake pedal
   - (c) a liquid fuel used in cars

6. brakes
   - (a) devices to stop a car
   - (b) devices to keep engine noise down
   - (c) safety straps to hold you in your seat

7. muffler
   - (a) device that steers a car
   - (b) headlight
   - (c) device to keep engine noise down

8. toll
   - (a) money you must pay to use a highway
   - (b) hot drinks
   - (c) system to start a car

9. speed limit
   - (a) end of the road
   - (b) stoplight
   - (c) fastest speed allowed

10. inspection
    - (a) machine that makes a car go
    - (b) checking of a car's condition
    - (c) short nap

Name _____

Date _____

(BONUS! Continue to circle the correct definition for each word.)

11. seat belt
   (a) strap to hold up your pants
   (b) strap for walking your dog
   (c) strap to hold you in your seat

12. coolant
   (a) fluid that makes the car's engine go
   (b) fluid that makes the car's engine cooler
   (c) box to keep sodas cool in

13. fuel
   (a) a liquid for your car
   (b) a type of tire for your car
   (c) food for your family's dinner

14. ignition
   (a) time off from work
   (b) device that stops your car
   (c) system for starting a car

15. oil
   (a) money you pay to use a road
   (b) greasy engine liquid
   (c) another word for gasoline

16. windshield
   (a) roof of your car
   (b) back end of your car
   (c) screen in front of people in your car

17. hood
   (a) cover over your car's engine
   (b) cover over the back of your car
   (c) bright light on the front of your car

18. tire
   (a) rubber that covers a wheel
   (b) flames that burn
   (c) measure of speed

19. headlight
   (a) light at the back of a car
   (b) light at the front of a car
   (c) light inside a car

20. automobile
   (a) another word for *train*
   (b) another word for *road*
   (c) another word for *car*

SENTENCE SENSE

Name _____

Date _____

Choose an ending that makes sense for each sentence. Circle the letter in front of the ending you choose. The vocabulary word or words in each sentence are underlined.

1. A driver's <u>license</u> shows that you
   (a) are legally allowed to drive.
   (b) have finished high school.
   (c) can dance and sing.

2. The signs changed from 50 <u>mph</u> to 30 <u>mph</u>. Dom did what the signs said and
   (a) drove the car much faster.
   (b) stopped the car and parked it.
   (c) slowed down the car.

3. A <u>seat</u> <u>belt</u>
   (a) is part of the engine.
   (b) holds up your pants.
   (c) holds you safely in your seat.

4. When a car does not have enough <u>coolant</u>,
   (a) the engine gets very hot.
   (b) the engine gets very cold.
   (c) the car runs out of gas.

5. You must <u>register</u> your car
   (a) before you can legally drive it.
   (b) or the engine won't start.
   (c) in the swimming pool.

6. <u>Fuel</u> is
   (a) the juice of apples.
   (b) what makes an engine run.
   (c) a wall covering.

7. When the car's <u>engine</u> did not work,
   (a) the car ran very well.
   (b) the car did not run.
   (c) the sun did not rise.

8. Put the key in the <u>ignition</u> switch and turn it
   (a) so the car will start.
   (b) so the car will stop.
   (c) so the water will freeze.

9. You pump <u>gas</u> into your car
   (a) when you are asleep.
   (b) in a hospital.
   (c) at a gas station.

10. Check to be sure there's enough <u>oil</u>
    (a) on the TV screen.
    (b) in the sugar bowl.
    (c) in your engine.

(BONUS! Continue to choose an ending that makes sense for each sentence.)

11. A car's <u>windshield</u> protects the
    (a) gas tank.
    (b) people inside the car.
    (c) tires.

12. The car's <u>brakes</u> did not work, so
    (a) the car stopped right away.
    (b) the car did not stop or slow down.
    (c) the car turned blue.

13. Open the <u>hood</u>
    (a) to turn on the lights.
    (b) to smell the flowers.
    (c) to look at the engine.

14. When a <u>tire</u> gets worn out, you must replace it with
    (a) a good tire.
    (b) a muffler.
    (c) a headlight.

15. A car's <u>headlights</u>
    (a) make the car stop.
    (b) make the engine go.
    (c) light up the road at night.

16. Our whole family got into the <u>automobile</u>
    (a) and sailed across the ocean in it.
    (b) and drove to Florida in it.
    (c) and flew into space in it.

17. The race driver took off the <u>muffler</u>
    (a) so the engine would sound very quiet.
    (b) so the engine would sound very loud.
    (c) and ate it.

18. The truck driver paid a <u>toll</u>
    (a) to use the highway.
    (b) to watch the movie.
    (c) to buy a muffler.

19. A <u>speed limit</u> of 30 mph means
    (a) you must drive at least 50 miles per hour.
    (b) you must stop.
    (c) you must not drive faster than 30 miles per hour.

20. During an <u>inspection</u>, a car
    (a) does well if it's in a bad condition.
    (b) should not have any brakes.
    (c) is checked to be sure it is in good condition.

Unit 8
SHOPPING WORDS

EXERCISE 1
SHOPPING WORD SENSE

Name _____

Date _____

Read each word below and its definition. Rewrite each word in the blanks next to its definition.

1.	payment	money paid in return for something	_ _ **y** _ _ _ _
2.	discount	amount taken off the regular price	_ _ _ _ **o** _ _ _
3.	guarantee	promise to repair, replace, or pay for a product if it has a defect; or, to give a guarantee	_ **u** _ _ _ _ _ _ _
4.	exchange	to replace one product with another; or, the act of exchanging	_ _ **c** _ _ _ _ _
5.	sale	exchange of things for money; selling something for less than usual	_ **a** _ _
6.	refund	to pay back; or, the money paid back	_ _ _ _ _ **n**
7.	rebate	return of part of a payment	_ _ **b** _ _ _
8.	defect	flaw; something wrong with a product	_ **e** _ _ _ _
9.	layaway	item put aside for a customer who pays a deposit and finishes paying later	_ **a** _ _ _ _ _
10.	warranty	written guarantee to repair or replace parts that have defects	**w** _ _ _ _ _ _ _
11.	installment	one of a series of payments of a total amount owed	**i** _ _ _ _ _ _ _ _ _ _
12.	sales tax	tax (money paid to the government) added to the price of items sold	_ _ _ _ **s** _ _ _
13.	return	to bring back; or, the item returned	_ **e** _ _ _ _
14.	sales slip	piece of paper recording a sale	_ _ _ _ **s** _ _ _ _
15.	shoplift	to take goods from a store without paying for them	_ **h** _ _ _ _ _ _
16.	customer	person who buys something	_ _ _ _ _ _ **o** _ _
17.	price	amount of money something costs	**p** _ _ _ _
18.	purchase	to buy, to get by paying money; or, something purchased	**p** _ _ _ _ _ _ _
19.	charge	to ask as a price; to agree to pay for something later	_ _ _ _ _ _ **e**
20.	credit card	small card used to charge things and pay later	_ **r** _ _ _ _ _ _ _ _ _

BONUS! The boxed letters spell out a sentence. What does it say? (Write it out here if you want:)

86   *200 Words You Need to Know*

Name _____

Date _____

Each sentence below has a word missing. Fill in each blank with a word that makes sense from the list at the top of this page. Check off each word in the list as you use it.

payment   exchanges   defect
discount   sale   layaway
guarantee   refund   warranty
                  rebate

1. The new car came with a two-year _w_ _ _r_ _ _ _ _n_ _t_ _ on most of its parts.

2. Save money by not buying until things are on _ _ _ _l_ _ .

3. Gene's new radio had a _ _ _e_ _ _ _c_ _ , so it wouldn't play.

4. Because the radio came with a _g_ _ _ _ _r_ _a_ _ _ _e_ _ , the maker fixed the defect at no cost to Gene.

5. To get a _ _ _b_ _ _t_ _ , you usually have to send your sales slip to the maker of the product.

6. The monthly _p_ _ _y_ _ _ _ _n_ _ on my car loan is $215.

7. Because the store sign said "No _ _x_ _c_ _ _ _ _n_ _g_ _ _ ," Tawana could not return the blue jeans she had bought.

8. When Prem finished paying for the coat that was on _l_ _ _ _a_ _w_ _ _ , he was able to take it home from the store.

9. The refrigerator had a small dent, so the store sold it at a _ _ _i_ _ _c_ _ _ _n_ _ .

10. Reggie brought the broken record back to the store and got a _ _ _ _f_ _u_ _ _ .

200 Words You Need to Know

Name _____

Date _____

(BONUS! Continue to fill in the blanks from the word list at the top of this page.)

installment	sales slip	purchase
sales tax	shoplift	charge
return	customer	credit card
	price	

11. When you r __ __ u __ __ an item to the store where you bought it, bring the sales slip.

12. The __ a __ e __ s __ __ __ shows the price of the item and the date you bought it.

13. Use your __ r __ d __ __ __ __ r d when you don't want to pay for something at the time you buy it.

14. A credit counts toward the __ u r __ __ a __ __ price of any item at the store.

15. When you __ h __ r __ __ your purchase, you agree to pay for it later.

16. You usually pay back an i __ __ t a __ l __ __ n t loan with one payment each month.

17. Most states charge a s __ l __ __ t __ __ on things that are sold.

18. When you shop, check the __ r i __ __ of the same item at several different stores.

19. A person who buys something is a c __ s t __ m __ __ .

20. To __ h o __ l __ f __—to take goods from a store without paying for them—is to steal.

HIDDEN WORDS

Name _____

Date _____

Read the following story. Draw a line under the words from the list below when you find them in the story. Check off each word in the list as you find it. The first one is done.

payment	refund	installments	customer
discount	rebate	sales tax	✔ price
guarantee	defect	return	purchase
exchange	layaway	sales slip	charge
sale	warranty	shoplift	credit card

A smart shopper needs to know some basic facts. Check the <u>price</u> of each item you want to purchase. Can you buy the item on sale or at a discount? Is a rebate offered? Remember that your payment will include sales tax. Ask the store if a customer can return an item for a refund or an exchange. You'll probably need your sales slip to do this, so save it. Also find out if the item comes with a warranty or a guarantee against any defect.

Do you have enough cash to pay in full? If not, ask if you can put the item on layaway or charge it. If you use a credit card, you may be able to pay in installments. But of course, don't shoplift!

Now write each word you marked in the story on the lines below.

price _____   _____   _____

_____   _____   _____

_____   _____   _____

_____   _____   _____

_____   _____   _____

_____   _____

_____

LUCKY LISTS

Name _____

Date _____

Each word in the list at the top of this page belongs in one of the categories listed below. Write each word under the category it belongs to. The first one in each category is done for you. Check off each word in the list as you use it.

✔ payment   ✔ sale   layaway   return   price
✔ discount   refund   warranty   sales slip   purchase
✔ guarantee   rebate   installment   shoplift   charge
   exchange   defect   sales tax   customer   credit card

Begins with a letter between *A* and *D*

discount

_____

_____

_____

_____

Begins with a letter between *E* and *L*

guarantee

_____

_____

_____

Begins with a letter between *M* and *R*

payment

_____

_____

_____

_____

Begins with a letter between *S* and *Z*

sale

_____

_____

_____

_____

PUZZLE TIME

Name _____

Date _____

Fill in the boxes in the puzzle with words that fit from the word list at the top of this page. Check the words off in the list as you use them. The first letter (and sometimes another one) of each word is given. The first one is done for you.

✔ payment   sale   layaway   return   price
  discount   refund   warranty   sales slip purchase
  guarantee rebate   installment shoplift   charge
  exchange   defect   sales tax   customer   credit card

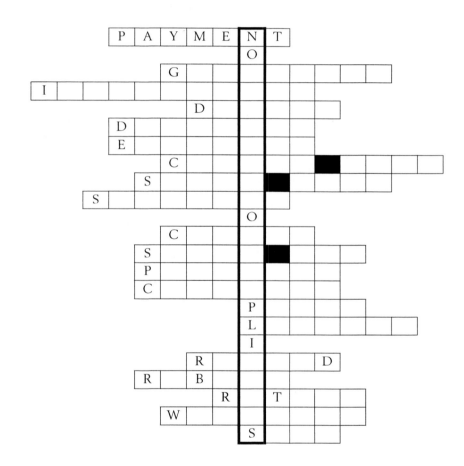

BONUS! The puzzle has a secret silly sentence. It reads from the top of the puzzle down. Write the puzzle's secret silly sentence here:

_____

     200 Words You Need to Know

WHAT'S MISSING?

Name _____

Date _____

A word (or two together) is missing from each sentence. Choose a word (or two together) from the list that makes sense and write it in the blank for each sentence. Check off each word in the list as you use it. The first one is done.

1. You pay less when things are on ___*sale*___ .

2. A _____ off the regular price saves money, too.

3. Someone who _____ may be arrested.

4. Randy paid a deposit and left the coat at the store on

   _____ .

5. When you buy an item, you _____ it.

6. Examine an item to be sure it has no _____ .

7. The _____ is how much something costs.

8. My _____ payment is due on the 15th of each month.

9. A store clerk should greet each _____ with a smile.

10. A _____ returns part of your payment.

11. A _____ usually returns all of your payment.

12. Some stores don't allow you to _____ or exchange what you buy.

13. Sometimes it's handy to charge things with your

    _____ _____ .

14. "No credit" means you can't _____ your purchase.

BONUS! If you have filled in all the blanks above, keep going and fill in these blanks, too.

15. A _____ _____ is a percent of the sales price.

16. A _____ is a written guarantee.

17. A product with a _____ will be fixed by the maker.

18. A _____ _____ is also called a sales check or receipt.

19. _____ in full is expected in 90 days.

20. I must _____ my new blouse for one that's smaller.

payment

discount

guarantee

exchange

✔ sale

refund

rebate

defect

layaway

warranty

installment

sales tax

return

sales slip

shoplifts

customer

price

purchase

charge

credit card

200 Words You Need to Know

DAFFY DEFINITIONS

Name _____

Date _____

Choose the correct definition for each word. Circle the letter in front of the definition you choose.

1. payment
   (a) money paid
   (b) bill
   (c) department store

2. discount
   (a) long story
   (b) extra fee charged
   (c) amount taken off regular price

3. guarantee
   (a) defect
   (b) promise to repair any defect
   (c) purchase price

4. exchange
   (a) added time
   (b) replace one thing with another
   (c) shoplift

5. sale
   (a) selling for less than usual
   (b) selling for more than usual
   (c) high price

6. refund
   (a) shelter
   (b) improvement
   (c) return of money paid

7. rebate
   (a) return of all of a payment
   (b) sales tax
   (c) return of part of a payment

8. defect
   (a) sneaker
   (b) something wrong with a product
   (c) excellence

9. layaway
   (a) item put aside for a customer
   (b) small couch
   (c) escaped prisoner

10. warranty
    (a) refund
    (b) rebate
    (c) written guarantee

Name _____

Date _____

(BONUS! Continue to choose the correct definition for each word.)

11. installment
    (a) one of a series of payments
    (b) Western movie
    (c) pavement

12. sales tax
    (a) charge added to cost of items sold
    (b) purchase price
    (c) discount off regular price

13. return
    (a) to purchase
    (b) to bring back
    (c) to travel a long way

14. sales slip
    (a) credit card
    (b) paper that records a purchase
    (c) check

15. shoplift
    (a) pay for goods
    (b) put goods on layaway
    (c) take goods without paying for them

16. customer
    (a) person who buys something
    (b) store manager
    (c) salesclerk

17. price
    (a) rebate
    (b) what something costs
    (c) refund

18. purchase
    (a) to shoplift
    (b) to return
    (c) to buy

19. charge
    (a) to cook on a grill
    (b) to exchange
    (c) to ask as a price

20. credit card
    (a) what you use to charge things
    (b) card you use to pay cash
    (c) sales slip

Choose an ending that makes sense for each sentence. Circle the letter in front of the ending you choose. The vocabulary word in each sentence is underlined.

1. Each time Darryl made a <u>payment</u>,
   (a) the store got smaller.
   (b) he owed less money.
   (c) the store closed.

2. Dad bought the washer at a <u>discount</u>,
   (a) so he paid more for it.
   (b) so he paid less for it.
   (c) so he got it for free

3. Keisha went to the store to <u>exchange</u> her ice skates
   (a) for another larger pair.
   (b) because she wanted to keep them.
   (c) into the ice.

4. The grocery store gave Uncle Albert a <u>refund</u>
   (a) for his headache.
   (b) for the sour milk he had bought.
   (c) for his warranty.

5. Because the radio came with a <u>rebate</u> offer,
   (a) we got $5 back from the maker.
   (b) we had to pay $5 extra when we bought it.
   (c) the maker promised it would have a defect.

6. The engine had a <u>defect</u>,
   (a) so it ran perfectly.
   (b) so the buyer was pleased with it.
   (c) so it needed to be fixed.

7. Read your <u>warranty</u> to find out
   (a) how many defects the product has.
   (b) how much sales tax to pay.
   (c) what defects will be repaired or parts replaced.

8. A person who <u>shoplifts</u>
   (a) pays for the goods he or she takes from the store.
   (b) steals goods from a store.
   (c) returns goods to a store.

9. When the <u>price</u> of coffee got very high, my brother
   (a) had to pay more for the coffee.
   (b) paid less than usual for the coffee.
   (c) didn't have to pay anything for the coffee.

10. When you <u>purchase</u> something, you
    (a) burn it.
    (b) rebate it.
    (c) buy it.

(BONUS! Continue to choose the correct ending for each sentence.)

11. My radio had a <u>guarantee</u>, so when it broke down,
    (a) I threw it in the trash.
    (b) I got a new one from the maker of the radio.
    (c) I lost a lot of money.

12. When I bought my sneakers on <u>sale</u>,
    (a) I saved a lot of money.
    (b) I paid a lot more for them.
    (c) I cooked them for dinner.

13. Selena put her in-line skates on <u>layaway</u> so she could
    (a) never afford to pay for them.
    (b) sleep on them.
    (c) pay for them over a period of time.

14. I paid each <u>installment</u> that I owed
    (a) all at once.
    (b) once every month.
    (c) when I first bought my car.

15. Once the <u>sales tax</u> was figured in, Lonnie's bill
    (a) was higher.
    (b) was lower.
    (c) was just the same.

16. You might <u>return</u> something you bought if
    (a) you really liked it.
    (b) you had never bought it.
    (c) it turned out that it didn't fit well.

17. A <u>sales slip</u> shows
    (a) how long your skirt is.
    (b) what you bought and what you paid for it.
    (c) that you fell down while you were shopping.

18. A happy <u>customer</u> is someone who is
    (a) charged too much.
    (b) treated well.
    (c) told to go away.

19. When you <u>charge</u> something, you
    (a) pay for it right then and there.
    (b) never have to pay for it.
    (c) pay for it later.

20. You use a <u>credit card</u>
    (a) to pay for something later.
    (b) to shoplift.
    (c) to build sand castles.

Unit 9

MONEY WORDS

MONEY WORD SENSE

Name _____

Date _____

Read each word below and its definition. Rewrite each word in the blanks next to its definition.

1. deposit — to put money in a bank; or, money put in a bank or given as part of a payment
   _ _ [p] _ _ _ _

2. dollar — basic unit of money worth 100 cents
   _ _ _ _ [a] _

3. money order — a paper ordering payment of a certain amount of money
   _ _ _ _ [y] _ _ _ _ _ _

4. bill — piece of paper money; or, a notice that you owe money
   _ [i] _ _

5. nickel — coin worth 5 cents
   [n] _ _ _ _ _

6. cent — coin also called a penny; 100 cents make one dollar
   [c] _ _ _

7. quarter — coin worth 25 cents
   _ _ [a] _ _ _ _

8. passbook — book showing the deposits and withdrawals in a bank account; bankbook
   _ _ _ _ [s] _ _ _

9. cash — money, both coins and paper bills
   _ _ _ [h]

10. coin — small piece of metal used as money
    _ [o] _ _

11. service charge — fee you pay to a bank or a business to keep your account
    _ _ [r] _ _ _ _ _ _ _ _ _ _ _

12. amount — total; what something adds up to
    _ _ _ _ [u] _ _

13. savings — money that you save or set aside to use later
    _ _ _ _ _ _ [s]

14. dime — coin worth 10 cents
    _ _ _ [e]

15. ATM — automatic teller machine; use it to get money out of your account
    [a] _ _

16. balance — amount left over or remaining
    _ _ _ _ _ [c] _

17. withdraw — to take money out of an account
    _ _ _ [h] _ _ _ _

18. interest — fee paid to use money
    _ _ _ [e] _ _ _ _

19. account — record or list of money paid out or received
    _ _ [c] _ _ _ _

20. check — written order to a bank to pay a certain amount of money from an account
    _ _ _ _ [k]

BONUS! The boxed letters spell out a sentence. What does it say? (Write it out here if you want:)

Name _____

Date _____

Each sentence below has a word (or two together) missing. Fill in each blank with a word that makes sense from the list at the top of this page. Check off each word in the list as you use it.

deposit   bill   cash
dollar   nickel   coin
money order   cent   dime
                 quarter

1. Aunt Marta paid me one __ __ _l_ __ _a_ __ to go to the store for her.

2. Each stick of hard candy cost one __ __ _m_ __ .

3. Each gumball cost one __ _i_ __ _k_ __ __ .

4. You can't buy many things for one __ __ _n_ __ .

5. What kind of __ _o_ __ __ do you put in that vending machine?

6. Katie's neighbors paid her for baby-sitting with a 5-dollar __ __ __ _l_ .

7. My father mailed a _m_ __ __ _e_ __   __ _r_ _d_ __ __ to our landlord to pay the rent.

8. Henry used his extra __ _u_ _a_ __ _t_ __ __ to play a video game at the arcade.

9. I always _d_ __ __ _o_ _s_ __ _t_ part of my paycheck in my savings account.

10. At the end of each day, the store manager took all the __ __ __ _h_ to the bank.

200 Words You Need to Know

Name _____

Date _____

(BONUS! Continue to fill in the blanks from the word list at the top of this page.)

service charge	passbook	interest
amount	ATM	account
savings	balance	check
	withdraw	

11. When you keep money in a bank, you have an __ __ c __ u n __ with that bank.

12. You can keep money in a checking account or a s __ v i __ __ __ account.

13. When you have a checking account, you can pay for things by __ h __ c __ instead of in cash.

14. The bank usually collects a monthly fee called a s __ r v __ __ __

    c __ __ r g __ for a checking account.

15. When you put money into your savings account, the deposit is shown in your

    p __ __ s b __ o __ .

16. When you w __ t h __ __ a __ money from your account, the passbook shows that, too.

17. The last amount shown in the passbook is your __ a l __ __ c __ .

18. The balance is the __ m __ u n __ of money you have in the account.

19. The money you earn on a bank account is called __ __ t __ __ e s __ .

20. You can use an __ T __ to see how much money is in your checking account.

200 Words You Need to Know

HIDDEN WORDS

Name _____

Date _____

Read the following story. Draw a line under the words from the list below when you find them in the story. Check off each word in the list as you find it. The first one is done.

deposit	cent	service charge	balance
dollar	quarter	amount	withdraw
money order	cash	✔ savings	interest
bills	coins	passbook	account
nickel	dime	ATM	check

Yesterday I went to the bank to put some money into my <u>savings</u> account. First I counted the coins—each cent, nickel, dime, and quarter—and then the dollar bills. I wrote the total amount of cash on the deposit slip. I gave the slip and my passbook to the teller. When the teller gave me back the bankbook, it showed how much interest I had earned, and it also showed my new balance.

Today I had to withdraw some money, so I used the ATM. I also cashed a check and bought a money order. The bank collects a service charge when it cashes checks for people who don't have accounts at that bank.

Now write each word you marked in the story on the lines below.

savings _____   _____   _____

_____   _____   _____

_____   _____   _____

_____   _____   _____

_____   _____   _____

_____   _____

LUCKY LISTS

Name _____

Date _____

Each word in the list at the top of this page belongs in one of the categories listed below. Write each word under the category it belongs to. The first one in each category is done for you. Check off each word in the list as you use it.

✔ deposit	nickel	coin	savings	withdraw
dollar	cent	dime	passbook	interest
✔ money order	✔ quarter	service charge	ATM	account
✔ bill	cash	amount	balance	check

Begins with a letter between _A_ and _B_

bill
_____
_____
_____

Begins with a letter between _C_ and _H_

deposit
_____
_____
_____
_____
_____

Begins with a letter between _I_ and _P_

money order
_____
_____
_____

Begins with a letter between Q and Z

quarter
_____
_____
_____
_____

Name _____

Date _____

Fill in the boxes in the puzzle with words that fit from the word list at the top of this page. Check the words off in the list as you use them. The first letter (and sometimes another one) of each word is given. The first one is done for you.

deposit	nickel	coin	savings	withdraw
dollar	cent	✔ dime	passbook	interest
money order	quarter	service charge	ATM	account
bill	cash	amount	balance	check

BONUS! The puzzle has a secret silly sentence. It reads from the top of the puzzle down. Write the puzzle's secret silly sentence here:

_____

A word (or two together) is missing from each sentence. Choose a word (or two together) from the list that makes sense and write it in the blank for each sentence. Check off each word in the list as you use it. The first one is done.

1. We paid by __*check*__ instead of in cash.

2. Both coins and bills are _____ .

3. A coin worth 1 _____ is called a penny.

4. A coin worth 5 cents is called a _____ .

5. A coin worth 10 cents is called a _____ .

6. A coin worth 25 cents is called a _____ .

7. Abraham Lincoln's picture is on the 5-dollar _____ .

8. There are 100 cents in each _____ .

9. A quarter is a kind of _____ .

10. A _____ _____ and a check both order the payment of a certain amount of money.

11. Mari had to pay a $5 _____ _____ every month on her checking account.

12. Another word for bankbook is _____ .

13. The amount you still owe on a loan is the _____ .

14. Tony had to _____ the money he needed from his savings account.

BONUS! If you have filled in all the blanks above, keep going and fill in these blanks, too.

15. The _____ left in the account was Tony's new balance.

16. Tavielle used the _____ to get some cash from her account.

17. The _____ rate on the loan was 8 percent.

18. Robin made a _____ into her savings account.

19. You can put money you don't want to use right away into a _____ account.

20. Money you need soon can go into a checking _____ .

deposit

dollar

money order

bill

nickel

cent

quarter

dime

cash

coin

service charge

amount

savings

passbook

ATM

balance

withdraw

interest

account

✔ check

Name _____

Date _____

Choose the correct definition for each word. Circle the letter in front of the definition you choose.

1. deposit
   - (a) to put money in a bank
   - (b) to take money out of a bank
   - (c) to rob a bank

2. dollar
   - (a) unit of money worth 100 cents
   - (b) item worn around the neck
   - (c) coin worth 10 cents

3. money order
   - (a) 5-dollar bill
   - (b) menu
   - (c) paper ordering payment of money

4. bill
   - (a) coin worth 5 cents
   - (b) notice that money is owed
   - (c) paperback book

5. nickel
   - (a) dollar bill
   - (b) coin worth 25 cents
   - (c) coin worth 5 cents

6. cent
   - (a) penny
   - (b) one dollar
   - (c) quarter

7. quarter
   - (a) coin worth 1 cent
   - (b) coin worth 25 cents
   - (c) coin worth 50 cents

8. dime
   - (a) penny
   - (b) coin worth 10 cents
   - (c) dollar bill

9. cash
   - (a) red spots on the skin
   - (b) checks
   - (c) coins and bills

10. coin
    - (a) small piece of metal used as money
    - (b) piece of paper money
    - (c) stick that helps you walk

Name _____

Date _____

(BONUS! Continue to choose the correct definition for each word.)

11. service charge
    - (a) coin
    - (b) loan
    - (c) fee paid to a bank

12. amount
    - (a) saddle
    - (b) total
    - (c) high hill

13. savings
    - (a) cash spent today
    - (b) grocery bill
    - (c) money set aside

14. passbook
    - (a) bankbook
    - (b) novel
    - (c) textbook

15. ATM
    - (a) automatic teller machine
    - (b) accounts to market
    - (c) a total mess

16. balance
    - (a) bill
    - (b) amount left
    - (c) form of dance

17. withdraw
    - (a) open an account
    - (b) take money out of an account
    - (c) put money into an account

18. interest
    - (a) paper money
    - (b) coin worth 10 cents
    - (c) fee paid for use of money

19. account
    - (a) record of money
    - (b) total
    - (c) penny

20. check
    - (a) dollar bill
    - (b) written order to pay money
    - (c) nickel or dime

Name _____

Date _____

Choose an ending that makes sense for each sentence. Circle the letter in front of the ending you choose. The vocabulary word in each sentence is underlined.

1. When you <u>deposit</u> money into your account,
    (a) your balance goes up.
    (b) your balance goes down.
    (c) your balance goes down to zero.

2. Alicia used her <u>dollar</u> bill
    (a) to freeze the water.
    (b) to comb her hair.
    (c) to buy a milkshake.

3. The video game cost a <u>quarter</u> to play, so I put
    (a) 5 cents in the machine.
    (b) 25 cents in the machine.
    (c) 10 cents in the machine.

4. The gum cost a <u>dime</u>, so I gave the clerk
    (a) 10 cents.
    (b) 50 cents.
    (c) 5 cents.

5. The <u>coin</u> my sister found was a
    (a) dollar bill.
    (b) nickel.
    (c) check.

6. Star's <u>savings</u> account
    (a) had a $50 balance.
    (b) shook hands with the bank teller.
    (c) was 50 feet tall.

7. Andre went to the <u>ATM</u>
    (a) to get a burger and fries.
    (b) to watch a movie.
    (c) to get some cash.

8. When you <u>withdraw</u> money from your account,
    (a) your balance goes up.
    (b) your balance goes down.
    (c) your balance stays the same.

9. The <u>interest</u> you earn on a bank account
    (a) adds money to the account.
    (b) takes money away from the account.
    (c) brings the account down to zero.

10. When you're paid by <u>check</u>,
    (a) you get a lot of cash.
    (b) you get a lot of coins.
    (c) you get a paper ordering a bank to pay you money.

Name _____

Date _____

(BONUS! Continue to choose the correct ending for each sentence.)

11. I sent a <u>money order</u> to my sister so she would get some
    (a) cash.
    (b) information.
    (c) rules for living.

12. A 5-dollar <u>bill</u>
    (a) tastes good.
    (b) is a coin.
    (c) is money.

13. Moriah spent a <u>nickel</u> on a
    (a) 10-cent stick of gum.
    (b) 5-cent piece of candy.
    (d) 50-cent soda.

14. *Penny* is another word for
    (a) a one-dollar bill.
    (b) a dime.
    (c) a cent.

15. When I pay <u>cash</u>, I pay with
    (a) dollar bills and coins.
    (b) two or three checks.
    (c) cakes and candies.

16. My bank charges a <u>service charge</u> for
    (a) my account every month.
    (b) doing my laundry.
    (c) buying my groceries.

17. The <u>amount</u> I pay is
    (a) the amount I feel like paying.
    (b) the amount I owe for what I buy.
    (c) never more than one dollar.

18. My <u>passbook</u> told me that
    (a) the moon was full.
    (b) I had never had a bank account.
    (c) I had $200 in my account.

19. The <u>balance</u> in your account tells you that
    (a) you are in good health.
    (b) your garden is growing well.
    (c) you have a certain amount in your account.

20. Your bank <u>account</u> is where you keep your
    (a) pets.
    (b) money.
    (c) relatives.

Unit 10

JOB WORDS

JOB WORD SENSE

Name _____

Date _____

Read each word below and its definition. Rewrite each word in the blanks next to its definition.

1. wages — money paid for work — _ _ [g] _ _

2. sick leave — time off from work because of illness — _ _ _ _ _ _ _ _ [e]

3. benefits — helpful things given to workers in addition to wages and salary — _ _ _ _ _ _ [t] _

4. vacation — period off from work for rest and fun — _ _ _ _ [t] _ _ _

5. employee — person who works for someone else or a company — _ _ _ _ [o] _ _ _

6. worker — employee; person who works — [w] _ _ _ _ _

7. employment — job; working for pay — _ _ _ _ _ [o] _ _ _ _

8. employer — person or company that pays other people to work — _ _ _ _ _ _ [r]

9. workplace — place where people work — _ _ _ [k] _ _ _ _

10. overtime — time worked beyond regular hours — [o] _ _ _ _ _ _ _

11. bonus — money given in addition to regular pay — _ _ [n] _ _

12. tax — money paid to the government out of wages — [t] _ _

13. insurance — protection against loss or damage — [i] _ _ _ _ _ _ _

14. minimum wage — lowest amount a worker can be paid per hour, by law — _ _ _ _ _ [m] _ _ _ _ _

15. supervisor — person who directs the work of employees — _ _ _ [e] _ _ _ _ _

16. paid holiday — day or days off from work with pay — _ _ _ [d] _ _ _ _ _ _

17. salary — money paid for work — _ _ [a] _ _ _

18. income — money you receive from work — [i] _ _ _ _ _

19. hourly — by the hour — _ _ _ [l] _

20. paycheck — check that pays wages or salary — _ _ [y] _ _ _ _

BONUS! The boxed letters spell out a sentence. What does it say? (Write it out here if you want:)

110   *200 Words You Need to Know*

FUN FILL-INS

Name _____

Date _____

Each sentence below has a word (or two words together) missing. Fill in each blank with a word that makes sense from the list at the top of this page. Check off each word in the list as you use it.

wages   vacation   employer
sick leave   employee   workplace
benefits   worker   bonus
                   employment

1. An __ *m* *p* __ __ *y* __ *e* is a person who works for someone else.

2. An *e* __ __ __ *l* *o* __ __ *r* is someone, or a company, who pays someone else to work.

3. __ *m* __ *l* __ *y* *m* __ __ *t* is having a job, or being employed.

4. Bruce quit his job because the __ *a* *g* __ __ were so low.

5. No smoking is allowed in our __ *o* *r* __ __ *l* __ *c* __ .

6. The union wants every worker to have two weeks of paid
   v __ __ *a* *t* __ __ __ .

7. Each __ __ *r* *k* __ __ at the shoe factory got a bonus at Christmas.

8. The __ *o* __ *u* __ was extra money added to the regular wages.

9. __ *e* *n* __ *f* __ __ __ like medical insurance are an important part of what you are paid for a job.

10. When Miguel had to stay in the hospital, he went on
    __ __ __ *k* __ *e* *a* __ __ .

200 Words You Need to Know

Name _____

Date _____

(BONUS! Continue to fill in the blanks from the word list at the top of this page.)

overtime	minimum wage	income
tax	supervisor	hourly
insurance	paid holiday	paycheck
	salary	

11. My mother gets her __ __ *y* __ *h* *e* __ __ every Friday.

12. It is not legal to pay a worker less than the *m* __ *n* __ *m* __ __ __ __ *g* __ .

13. That company gives its workers one __ *a* __ __ __ *o* *l* __ __ *a* __ every month.

14. Health *i* __ __ *u* *r* __ __ *c* __ helps pay hospital and doctors' bills when you're sick.

15. You must report how much you earn each year on an __ *n* __ *o* __ __ tax return.

16. "Withholding" is money held out of a paycheck to pay the income __ __ *x* .

17. The file clerk's starting __ __ *l* *a* __ *y* was $200 per week.

18. You are usually paid extra for working __ *v* __ __ __ __ *m* __ .

19. When you are paid a certain amount for each hour you work, you are being paid __ *o* *u* __ *l* __ .

20. Kit asked his *s* __ *p* __ __ *v* *i* __ *o* __ what he should do first.

200 Words You Need to Know

Name _____

Date _____

Read the following story. Draw a line under the words from the list below when you find them in the story. Check off each word in the list as you find it. The first one is done.

wages	worker	bonus	paid holiday
sick leave	✔ employment	tax	salary
benefits	employer	insurance	income
vacation	workplace	minimum wage	hourly
employee	overtime	supervisor	paycheck

When you look for <u>employment</u>, you must ask some questions. What salary or hourly wages will you earn for a job? Will you still have enough income after tax is taken out of your paycheck? Does the job pay more than the minimum wage? Will you work and be paid for overtime? Ask the employer or supervisor what benefits each employee is given. Will you have health insurance? How often will you have a paid holiday and a vacation? Will you be paid when you're on sick leave? Can you expect a Christmas bonus? Also find out if each worker belongs to a labor union. Finally, look at where you'll be doing your job. Do the workplace conditions look good to you?

Now write each word you marked in the story on the lines below.

employment _____   _____

_____   _____   _____

_____   _____   _____

_____   _____   _____

_____   _____   _____

_____   _____

LUCKY LISTS

Name _____

Date _____

Each word in the list at the top of this page belongs in one of the categories listed below. Write each word under the category it belongs to. Some are done for you. Check off each word in the list as you use it.

✔ wages   employee   workplace   insurance   salary

✔ sick leave   worker   ✔ overtime   minimum wage   income

✔ benefits   employment   bonus   supervisor   hourly

     vacation   employer   tax   paid holiday   paycheck

Begins with a letter between *A* and *E*

benefits

_____

_____

_____

Begins with a letter between *F* and *O*

overtime

_____

_____

_____

Begins with a letter between *P* and *S*

sick leave

_____

_____

_____

Begins with a letter between *T* and *Z*

wages

_____

_____

_____

Name _____

Date _____

Fill in the boxes in the puzzle with words that fit from the word list at the top of this page. Check the words off in the list as you use them. The first letter (and sometimes another one) of each word is given. The first one is done for you.

✔ wages   employee   workplace   insurance   salary
sick leave   worker   overtime   minimum wage   income
benefits   employment   bonus   supervisor   hourly
vacation   employer   tax   paid holiday   paycheck

BONUS! The puzzle has a secret silly sentence. It reads from the top of the puzzle down. Write the puzzle's secret silly sentence here:

_____

Name _____

Date _____

A word (or two together) is missing from each sentence. Choose a word (or two together) from the list that makes sense and write it in the blank for each sentence. Check off each word in the list as you use it. The first one is done.

1. Another word for *employee* is ___*worker*___ .

2. Working for pay is called _____ .

3. Assembly-line _____ were $6 per hour.

4. Expect to be paid more when you work _____ .

5. Don't accept a job that pays less than the _____ _____ .

6. The job's _____ include health and life insurance.

7. An _____ who employs 500 workers can't supervise each worker directly.

8. Instead, a _____ directs a smaller group of workers.

9. Another word for *worker* is _____ .

10. Wages can be paid in cash or by a _____ .

11. The _____ wage at the repair shop is $7.

12. Al's _____ was paid once a week.

13. Each worker got a turkey as a Thanksgiving _____ .

14. My _____ is large and sunny.

BONUS! If you have filled in all the blanks above, keep going and fill in these blanks, too.

15. Workers pay an _____ tax on what they earn.

16. A _____ is money paid to the government.

17. Life _____ pays money to your family if you die.

18. The company doctor told Yvette to stay home on _____ _____ .

19. Christmas is a _____ _____ for most workers.

20. I always take my two weeks _____ in July.

wages

sick leave

benefits

vacation

employee

✔ worker

employment

employer

workplace

overtime

bonus

tax

insurance

minimum wage

supervisor

paid holiday

salary

income

hourly

paycheck

DAFFY DEFINITIONS

Name _____

Date _____

Choose the correct definition for each word. Circle the letter in front of the definition you choose.

1. wages
   - (a) sheets of paper
   - (b) money paid for work
   - (c) temper tantrums

2. sick leave
   - (a) dead plant
   - (b) vacation time
   - (c) time off from work for illness

3. benefits
   - (a) money paid to the government
   - (b) lost money
   - (c) helpful things given in addition to wages

4. vacation
   - (a) period of time off from work
   - (b) work hours
   - (c) relative

5. employee
   - (a) place where people work
   - (b) person who works for someone else
   - (c) person who pays others to work

6. worker
   - (a) employee
   - (b) money paid for work
   - (c) student

7. employment
   - (a) not having a job
   - (b) working for pay
   - (c) taking a vacation

8. employer
   - (a) worker
   - (b) person who works for someone else
   - (c) person who pays other people to work

9. workplace
   - (a) place where people work
   - (b) person who works
   - (c) book of stamps

10. bonus
    - (a) extra pay
    - (b) skeleton
    - (c) wages or salary

Name _____

Date _____

(BONUS! Continue to choose the correct definition for each word.)

11. overtime
   - (a) cooking device
   - (b) regular hours of work
   - (c) extra hours of work

12. tax
   - (a) helpful thing given to workers
   - (b) money paid to the government
   - (c) salary

13. insurance
   - (a) type of teaching
   - (b) protection against loss
   - (c) paycheck

14. minimum wage
   - (a) lowest hourly pay, by law
   - (b) highest hourly pay, by law
   - (c) the only legal rate of pay

15. supervisor
   - (a) person who directs employees' work
   - (b) type of factory
   - (c) baseball cap

16. paid holiday
   - (a) strike
   - (b) day off from work with pay
   - (c) sick leave

17. salary
   - (a) person who sails a boat
   - (b) lettuce and other raw vegetables
   - (c) money paid for work

18. income
   - (a) money you pay to others
   - (b) money you receive
   - (c) being inside a building

19. hourly
   - (a) by the hour
   - (b) weekly
   - (c) monthly

20. paycheck
   - (a) bills and coins
   - (b) breakfast cereal
   - (c) check that pays wages

Choose an ending that makes sense for each sentence. Circle the letter in front of the ending you choose. The vocabulary word or words in each sentence are underlined.

1. Deon took his <u>wages</u> and
   (a) put them in the bank.
   (b) made them into a thick soup.
   (c) wore them on his feet.

2. The <u>benefits</u> Cherelle wanted most were
   (a) bad working conditions.
   (b) family health insurance and child care payments.
   (c) high taxes.

3. When my cousin became an <u>employee</u> of that company,
   (a) he had a job.
   (b) he stopped working.
   (c) he didn't have a job.

4. Tiana became an <u>employer</u> when
   (a) she went on vacation.
   (b) she went to work for a friend.
   (c) she hired a friend to work for her.

5. When Rodney worked <u>overtime</u>,
   (a) he earned less money.
   (b) his weekly paycheck was bigger.
   (c) he had more spare time.

6. Li was glad he had medical <u>insurance</u>
   (a) to buy his food.
   (b) to pay his doctor's bills.
   (c) to pay for his vacation.

7. On our <u>paid</u> <u>holiday</u>, we all
   (a) went to work.
   (b) went to the beach.
   (c) did not get paid.

8. I count on my <u>salary</u>
   (a) to pay my rent.
   (b) to fill my bathtub.
   (c) to freeze the pond.

9. The family had a low <u>income</u>, so
   (a) they spent a lot of money on vacations.
   (b) they had a lot of extra cash.
   (c) it was hard to buy the children new shoes.

10. The <u>hourly</u> wage for the day care workers was
    (a) $850 per month.
    (b) $200 per week.
    (c) $6 per hour.

Name _____

Date _____

(BONUS! Continue to choose the correct ending for each sentence.)

11. When my sister went on <u>sick</u> <u>leave</u>, she
    (a) played sports and went dancing.
    (b) stayed home and tried to get well again.
    (c) went in to work every day.

12. I like to take my <u>vacation</u>
    (a) while I am at the office working.
    (b) while I am asleep.
    (c) in the summer so I can swim and play outdoors.

13. Tranh became a <u>worker</u> when he
    (a) became a student.
    (b) became an employee.
    (c) became a bonus.

14. <u>Employment</u> is
    (a) having a job.
    (b) having no way to earn money.
    (c) having a lot of relatives.

15. The <u>workplace</u> is where you
    (a) perform your job.
    (b) do your grocery shopping.
    (c) dance and have a party every day.

16. When you are paid a <u>bonus</u>,
    (a) you have money taken away.
    (b) your job is taken away.
    (c) you get extra pay.

17. Tina had to pay <u>tax</u> to
    (a) herself.
    (b) the government.
    (c) her lawn mower.

18. Aysha worked for the <u>minimum</u> <u>wage</u>, so she
    (a) earned the least amount the law allowed.
    (b) earned more than most people did.
    (c) earned no money at all.

19. Because he was a <u>supervisor</u>, Dennis
    (a) took orders from everyone.
    (b) ordered everyone in the company around.
    (c) was in charge of one group of workers.

20. When I got my <u>paycheck</u>, I went right out and
    (a) ate it.
    (b) spent it.
    (c) tore it up.